B L U E P R I N T
Phonics Activities
Resource Bank

Carol Cort

Stanley Thornes (Publishers) Ltd

Do you receive *BLUEPRINTS NEWS*?

Blueprints is an expanding series of practical teacher's ideas books and photocopiable resources for use in primary schools. Books are available for separate infant and junior age ranges for every core and foundation subject, as well as for an ever widening range of other primary teaching needs. These include **Blueprints Primary English** books and **Blueprints Resource Banks**. **Blueprints** are carefully structured around the demands of the National Curriculum in England and Wales, but are used successfully by schools and teachers in Scotland, Northern Ireland and elsewhere.

Blueprints provide:

- *Total curriculum coverage*
- *Hundreds of practical ideas*
- *Books specifically for the age range you teach*
- *Flexible resources for the whole school or for individual teachers*
- *Excellent photocopiable sheets – ideal for assessment and children's work profiles*
- *Supreme value.*

Books may be bought by credit card over the telephone and information obtained on **(01242) 577944**. Alternatively, photocopy and return this **FREEPOST** form to receive **Blueprints News**, our regular update on all new and existing titles. You may also like to add the name of a friend who would be interested in being on the mailing list.

Please add my name to the **BLUEPRINTS NEWS** mailing list.

Mr/Mrs/Miss/Ms _____

Home address _____

_____ Postcode _____

School address _____

_____ Postcode _____

Please also send **BLUEPRINTS NEWS** to:

Mr/Mrs/Miss/Ms _____

Address _____

_____ Postcode _____

To: Marketing Services Dept., Stanley Thornes Ltd, FREEPOST (GR 782), Cheltenham, GL50 1BR

First published in 1995 by:
Stanley Thornes (Publishers) Ltd
Ellenborough House
Wellington Street
CHELTENHAM GL50 1YW
England

A catalogue record for this book is available from the British Library.

ISBN 0–7487–3442–5

Typeset by Tech-Set, Gateshead, Tyne & Wear
Printed and bound in Great Britain by Redwood Books, Trowbridge, Wiltshire

97 98 99 00 / 10 9 8 7 6 5 4

CONTENTS

INTRODUCTION

The *Phonics Activities Resource Bank* is a comprehensive photocopiable compendium of 140 pages of activities and games for use alongside phonic programmes and the *Reading Activities Resource Bank*. Its aim is to develop a child's phonic ability through repetitive practice, to increase memory skills and to build self-confidence.

Most primary schools will have banks of reading equipment and activities, either bought or home-made, to support their reading and spelling programmes. This book provides a huge bank of such material ready made for use in the classroom that will save you both time and money. It allows you to prepare carefully graded, relevant activities and games at a fraction of the cost of commercially bought ones. It also means that a lost piece does not cause problems: you simply photocopy the sheet again and replace the piece.

The activities are highly versatile. They can be photocopied directly onto card or photocopied onto paper and then stuck onto card. The materials may be coloured and covered for permanent use, or quickly run off on paper for more immediate classroom use. You will find practical instructions in the next section, 'Making and using the activities.' Manufacturing the games is an ideal activity for parent helpers either at home or at school. As the cost of producing activities is minimal you can even send sheets of games home to be made up and practised with parents.

The *Phonics Activities Resource Bank* covers:

- Alphabetical order
- Alphabet sounds
- Short vowel sounds
- Initial blends
- Word endings
- Track games to provide more practice
- Vowel consonant blends
- Vowels with only one consonant between them, 'magic e' at the end
- Vowel blends
- 'ck' ending following a short vowel sound
- 'ke' ending following a long vowel sound
- 'c' or 'k' at the start of a word
- Softening of 'c' and 'g' when followed by an 'e' or 'i'.

Most of the games can be used flexibly with either individuals or groups and many have a self-correcting element so that they can be played without adult supervision. You will find general instructions for playing the games on pages 1–7.

All the games have been extensively trialled and played by real children in real classrooms. They are stimulating, fun to play – and they work. Once you have started to work with the activities we are sure that you will find this book yet another absolutely invaluable resource to return to again and again.

MAKING AND USING THE ACTIVITIES

GENERAL INSTRUCTIONS

The activities in this book can be prepared in three ways.

a) Photocopied directly onto card
b) Photocopied onto paper
c) As in b) and then glued onto card.

Preparation
1 Photocopy the sheets as required.
2 Colour the copies and then, if required, stick the paper onto card.
3 Cut out all the pieces.
4 Run a wide felt tipped pen around the edge of the cards to obtain a professional-looking finish.
   If the pen is used half on and half off the card no ruler is necessary. This technique may require some practice but it is worthwhile as considerable time can be saved. Each complete set should be edged with the same colour pen so that pieces can be returned to their correct places easily.

5 Cover all pieces, on both sides, with transparent adhesive plastic e.g. *Coverlon*®. Several cards can be covered at the same time.

6 Cut around the pieces leaving a small border. The cutting action seals the plastic sheets together. The activity is now ready for use.

MAKING AND PLAYING THE GAMES

Jigsaws
Copymasters 5, 8–11.
An activity for one child.

Objective of the activity
To provide self-correcting (and therefore confidence-building) material in a meaningful and repetitive way.

Preparation
a) Photocopy the required sheets and prepare as in the General Instructions.
b) Cut the jigsaws apart as shown opposite.

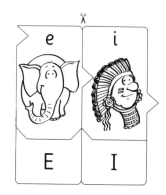

1

To use the activity
The child is given the jigsaw to sort into its correct alphabetical order.

Building activities
Copymasters 6–7, 76–7.
An activity for two–six children.
You will need:
One or two dice and three counters per child.

Objective of the activity
To build a child's self-confidence and memory span by providing repetitive practice of a phonetic sound.

Preparation
Each child has a set of equipment. The sets consist of the two prepared photocopied sheets and, if desired, word cards produced using the 'Find the pair' copymasters.
a) Photocopy the required number of sets.
b) Colour the copies.
c) Cut the building activity sheet numbered 2 into the component parts as shown on the base board.
d) Cover all the pieces, including the base board.
e) Velcro® pieces may be attached to the front of the base board and the back of the picture pieces using strong glue, e.g. PVA. This makes the activity easier to use.

To use the activity
1 Each child sets up his or her equipment as shown.
2 The children throw the dice in turn and the child with the highest score begins; play continues in a clockwise direction. When the dice is thrown the piece corresponding to the number thrown is collected and placed on the base board. If phonic cards are being used the first card must be read correctly before a piece can be collected.
3 The other children take their turns in the same way. If a child already has the piece corresponding to the number on the dice then he or she collects a counter instead. Three counters may be exchanged for a piece of the child's choice. The first child to fill his or her base board is the winner.

Find the pair
Copymasters 1–4, 23–4, 27–8, 31–4, 43, 67–8, 73–4, 78–9, 81–2, 87–90, 93–8, 125–6, 139–140.
An activity for two–three children.

Objective of the activity
To reinforce a phonic rule, each set being based on an individual phonic sound. The activity will improve a child's memory span and spelling.

Preparation
Each set of picture cards is immediately followed by the corresponding set of letters or words, both copymasters must be photocopied.
a) Photocopy the sheets required.
b) Colour and cut the cards as explained in the General Instructions on page 1.

At this point the cards should be marked with matching tabs so that one set can be used for several activities. Each pair must have a unique set of matching marks. By changing the colour, shape and position of the marks, several sets may be used together. (See Copymasters 43 and 85.)

c) Complete the preparation as in the General Instructions.

To use the activity
1 The cards are mixed up and then placed face down on the table in rows to form a rectangle.
2 Each child may, in turn, turn over any two cards. This needs to be done in such a way that all the children can have a good view. If the cards do not match he or she replaces them, face down, in their original positions.
3 If the cards selected are a pair, word matching picture, he or she keeps them and takes another turn. The child may do this until he or she fails to find a pair.
4 The activity continues until all the pairs have been found. The child with the most pairs is the winner.

Touch cards
Use the 'Find the pair' copymasters (see above).

Objective of the activity
To help build self-confidence by presenting phonic rules in a self-correcting (and therefore confidence-building) format.

Preparation
These cards are prepared using the 'Find the pair' cards.
a) Colour and cut out as in the General Instructions.
b) Glue each answer card onto its corresponding question card.
c) Cover the cards as usual.

There are many ways to use these cards.

Activity 1
For one child.
1 The touch cards are laid out with the words facing upwards.
2 The child points to a card, reads the word and then checks to see if he or she is right. If correct the child collects the card, if not it remains on the table and another card is chosen. The activity continues until all the cards have been collected.

Activity 2
For one child.
The same process is repeated but this time the answers are repeated to an adult. This helps build self-confidence because the words have already been learnt.

Activity 3
An activity for two children.
The cards are laid out on the table with the words facing upwards. The children take turns to read the words, choosing any card and checking the answer. Each child collects correctly read cards. When all the cards have been collected the child with the most is the winner.

Activity 4
An activity for two children.
1 The cards are placed in a pile, words facing upwards and the children take turns to read the words on the top card.

2 If the card is read correctly it is collected, if not it is placed in a new pile, with the pictures facing upwards, next to the original stack.

3 When the first pile is completed the wrongly read cards are turned over and the procedure is repeated until all the cards have been read correctly.

Self-correcting matching jigsaws
Copymasters as for 'Find the pair' cards.
An activity for one child.

Objective of the activity
To build self-confidence by providing a self-correcting method of phonic rules.

Preparation
Prepare as for 'Find the pair' cards.

The number of jigsaws given to a child should depend on the ability of the child. A set may be built up slowly or lengthened by joining two sets. Problem words can be carried forward and added to another set, thus providing further practice.

To use the activity
1 The cards are mixed up and then spread out face upwards.

2 The child looks at the word cards and tries to find the corresponding picture cards. The matching tabs are there to help.

3 When all the cards have been paired they should be checked and the child asked to read them.

Once a child is familiar with the answers, the cards can be used to play a game such as 'Find the pair' or 'Match the jigsaw'.

Match the jigsaw
Copymasters as for 'Find the pair'.
An activity for two children.

To use the activity
1 The cards are mixed up and half are placed face upwards on the table.

2 The second half are placed face up in a pile.

3 The first child takes the top card off the pile and he tries to match it with the cards already displayed. If it matches he takes the pair, if not the card is placed with those already on the table.

4 The second child now tries to match a card in the same way.

5 When all the cards from the pile have been used the game continues with the children collecting the pairs from the table. The winner is the child with the most cards.

Dominoes
Copymasters 15–17, 20–22, 29–30, 35, 49–50, 69, 72, 75, 80, 86, 99.
An activity for two children.

Objective of the activity
To provide repetitive practice of phonic rules. This improves not only a child's knowledge of a phonic rule but also his or her memory skills. (Phonic rules are listed on the Contents page.)

Preparation
a) Photocopy the required copymasters.
b) The phonic rule applying to each set may be highlighted or underlined on each card before cutting out the dominoes. Cut them out following the dotted lines.
c) Choose a starting card and mark it on the back.
d) Cover the cards as explained in the General Instructions.

To use the activity
1 The cards are divided equally between the two children.

2 The child with the starting card places it face upwards on the table.

3 The second child looks at his or her card and tries to find a match, word to picture or picture to word. If he or she has a suitable card it is placed to match.

4 The first child continues in the same way.

5 If the child does not have a matching card he or she misses that turn.

6 The winner is the first child to have no cards left.

Frog race track game
Copymasters 12–14.
An activity for two–three children.
You will need:
A dice and coloured counters.

Objective of the activity
To provide repetitive practice thereby building self-confidence.

Preparation
a) Photocopy the copymasters.
b) Colour and trim the copymasters and join them together.
c) Cover the track game in adhesive plastic as explained in the General Instructions.

To use the activity
1 Each child chooses a different coloured counter and places it on the start line.

2 Each player throws the dice and the one with the highest score begins by moving their counter the number of places shown on the dice.

3 Play continues with each child taking his or her turn and moving his or her counter according to the number shown on the dice.

4 The winner is the first child to reach the finish line.

Race the clock – lower and upper case
Copymasters 18 and 19.
An activity for one or two–four children.
You will need:
A stop clock. A small plastic tray would be useful for each child to store their tiles.

Objective of the activity
To provide repetitive practice of alphabetical order and to improve memory skills.

Preparation
a) Two copies of the copymaster are needed for each child.

3

b) Half the copies should be cut up into individual alphabet tiles, whilst the other half make the base boards as shown below.

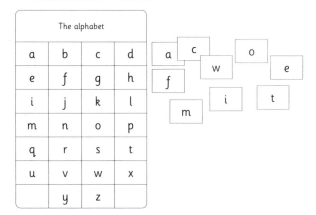

c) Colour the board. At this stage the vowels may be coloured to distinguish them from the consonants.
d) Cover all the pieces as explained in the General Instructions.

To use the activity
1 Each child has a base board and a complete set of matching alphabet letters.
2 The letters are placed face upwards on the table next to each child's base board.
3 The clock is started and each child races to place their alphabet tiles correctly on their board.
4 The first child to finish stops the clock and the time taken is recorded. The alphabet board is checked and if it has been completed correctly this child is the winner.
5 The game may be repeated with all the children trying to better the fastest time.
6 A single child may play the game by trying to improve on their own best time.

Vowel match
Copymasters 25–6.
An activity for two children.

Objective of the activity
To provide practice in recognising short vowel sounds.

Preparation
a) Photocopy the required copymasters.
b) Cut Copymaster 25 into individual tiles and Copymaster 26 into two base boards.
c) Colour and cover all the pieces as explained in the General Instructions.

To use the activity
1 Each child has a base board.
2 The picture cards are mixed and then placed face downwards in a pile.
3 The children take turns to pick up a tile and place it to match on a square on their base board.
4 If a vowel has already been covered the tile is placed in a new stack face upwards at the side of the original pile.
5 When all the original cards have been used the new pile is turned over and the game continues until one child fills their board.
6 The first child to fill their board is the winner.

Lotto
Copymasters 47–8, 83–4.
An activity for two children.

Objective of the activity
To provide practice in distinguishing between initial letter blends.

Preparing and using the activity
Follow the instructions for 'Vowel match' (above). For Copymasters 83–4, either sheet may be cut into lotto tiles.

The parachute race/Jack and the bean stalk/Humpty Dumpty
Copymasters 36–7, 38–9, 40–41 and 42 for vowel playing tiles.
An activity for two–six children.

The objective of the activity
To help a child to recognise and use short vowel sounds, thus building confidence.
You will need:
A dice.

Preparation
a) Photocopy the required copymasters. Each child needs a base board; the group of players share the vowel tiles from Copymaster 42.
b) Colour, cut out and cover all the pieces as explained in the General Instructions.

To use the activity
1 A base board is placed in front of each child.
2 The vowel letters are mixed up and then spread out face down in the centre of the table to form a 'tile bank'.
3 Each base board has a series of short words with their vowels missing.
4 Each child throws the dice, the child with the highest score begins and play continues in a clockwise direction.
5 The first child picks a vowel tile, examines it and decides whether it will fill the first space in his or her base board. If the vowel on the tile completes the word the tile is placed on the board. If the vowel does not complete a word it is returned to the tile bank.
6 The other children take their turns in the same way. The first child to fill all the spaces on their base board with the correct vowel tiles is the winner.

The game may be used by an individual child working against a timer.

Word wheels
Copymasters 44 (sl), 45 (gl), 46 (pl), 91 (ow), 112 (ew), 132 (ay).
An activity for one child or a group of children.

Objective of the activity
To reinforce phonic sound lessons thus improving a child's self-confidence.
You will need:
A brass split pin for each word wheel.

Preparation

a) Photocopy the required copymasters (see list above).

b) Colour, cut out and cover the copymaster as explained in the General Instructions.

c) Pierce a small hole through the centre of the base board and the wheel, push a split pin, from the front, through the centre of the wheel and then through the base board. The pin is then opened out and pressed flat on the back. A piece of tape should be placed over the points to prevent accidents.

To use the activity

The wheel is turned to find the words. Note that at this level every combination of letters produces a proper word.

The children should be asked to record the words they find. This can be extended and the child asked to include the words in sentences or even in a short story.

Double word wheel

Copymasters 103, 106, 108 and 110 for the word wheels; 109 and 111 for the base board; 107 for a work card.
An activity for one child or a group of children.

Objective of the activity

To provide practice in recognising words containing specific phonic sounds and to help to build self-confidence by enabling the child to correct their own work using the answer card. Note that not every combination of letters possible produces a 'proper' word.
You will need:
Two brass split pins per word wheel activity. (Small pieces of velcro are optional and can be used to produce base boards with changeable phonic letter squares and wheels.)

Preparation

a) Copy the required copymasters. For each word wheel activity you will need a base board, two wheels and a small letter square supplying the phonic sound to be practised. Note that care must be taken to ensure that the wheels are placed in their correct positions. They are labelled with a small R for right and L for left.

b) Cut out the copymasters, including the shaded squares on the lion base board.

c) Cover all the pieces as explained in the General Instructions.

d) Glue the letter square in place on the base board.

e) Pierce small holes in the centre of the wheels and at the points marked x on the base board.

To attach the word wheels and use the Leo base board: a split pin must be pushed, from the front, through the base board and then through the centre of the appropriate wheel. The pin is then opened out and pressed flat on the back. A piece of tape should be placed over the points to prevent accidents. Repeat with the second wheel. (The wheels are fixed behind the Leo base board and letters show through the cut out squares.)

To use Professor Penelope's word finder base board: push a split pin, from the front, through the word wheel and then through the base board. The pin is then opened out and pressed flat on the back. A piece of tape should be placed over the points to prevent accidents. Repeat with the second wheel. (The wheels are fixed to the front of Professor Penelope's word finder machine.)

To use the activity

The wheel is turned to find the words. Note that at this level not every combination of letters produces a proper word.

The children should be asked to record the words they find. This activity can be extended by asking the child to include the words in sentences or even in a short story.

Sliding strip word find

Copymasters 55, 57, 59 and 61 for Sam the Spaceman, Toby Tyrannosaurus, Wordal and Teddy characters; 51–4 and 63–6 for sliding letter strips; 56, 58, 60 and 62 for associated work sheets.

Copymasters 120–121 for Wanda Witch and -tch words; Copymasters 130–131 for The y to i machine.
An activity for one child.

The objective of the activity

To provide attractive, repetitive material to reinforce a phonic rule.
You will need:
Two small pieces of double-sided adhesive velcro.

Preparation

a) Photocopy the copymasters.

b) Colour the character base board.

c) Cut out the copymasters, remembering to re-cut the slots in the character base board.

d) Cover the pieces in transparent adhesive plastic as explained in the General Instructions, then re-cut the slots in the character using a single slit.

e) Attach the word base to the right or left of the slots, using the velcro strips or adhesive tape. Now thread the corresponding sliding strip through the slits from the back of the character base board. Only one word will show from the front; new words can, or course, be created by pulling the strip.

The circus race track game

Copymasters 70–71.
An activity for two–four children.

Objective of the activity

The aim of this activity is to give repetitive practice of a phonic rule chosen by the teacher. Thereby building a child's confidence in their ability to spell words following a learned rule.
You will need:
A dice and four sets of five counters, each set being a different colour. A set of word cards for each child.

Preparation

a) Photocopy the copymasters.

b) Colour. Make sure to colour one of the corner balloons to match each child's set of counters. Cut out, join and cover the sheets.

c) The question cards may be made up from any of the 'Find the pair' sets.

To use the activity

1 Each child chooses a starting arrow on the board and places their four coloured counters on the nearest balloons.
2 The children throw the dice and the child with the highest score begins.
3 The first child places his or her first counter on the arrow and then throws the dice. He or she then answers a question card and, if the answer is correct, moves forward the number shown on the dice.
4 The other children take their turns in the same way.
5 When a player's counter returns to his or her arrow it is placed within his or her balloon. The child then places the next counter on the arrow ready for his or her next turn.
6 The first child to place all their counters within their balloon is the winner.

The 'Jungle hunt track game' is produced and played in the same way. (Colour the corner flowers to match the children's counters.)

Throw the snowballs
Copymaster 92.
An activity for one child.

Objective of the activity
This activity provides practice of the 'ow' as in snow sound. The snowman image helps the child to remember the sound.
You will need:
A small piece of velcro.

Preparation
a) Photocopy Copymaster 92.
b) Colour, cut and cover all the pieces as explained in the General Instructions. Cut the copymaster to form a base board and individual 'snowballs'.
c) Stick small pieces of velcro (fluffy) onto the back of the snowballs.

To use the activity
1 The child throws the snowballs against the snowman's scarf, recording the words he or she finds.
2 The words can then be used to write sentences or to produce a short story.

Christmas tree game
Copymasters 100–102.
This game is produced and played in the same way as 'The parachute game' (see p. 4) but concentrates on the use of the vowel blends **ee**, **ea** and **ai**.

Snap!
Copymasters 113–116.
An activity for two children.

Objective of the activity
To provide repetitive practice using the **th**, **ch**, **wh**, **ph** and **sh** sounds.

Preparation
Colour, cut out and cover all the cards as explained in the General Instructions.

To use the activity
This is a pairing snap game in which only pairs are collected.
1 The cards are shuffled and dealt out between the children.
2 The first child places a card face upwards in the centre of the table and the second child places a card next to the first card.
3 If the underlined phonic sound of the two cards match, the first child to say 'Snap!' collects the two cards and places them to the side to be counted at the end of the game. The game continues with each child in turn adding a card to their central pile and shouting 'Snap!' if the top cards match.
4 At the end of each round any cards left in the central piles are re-shuffled and dealt. The game continues until all the cards have been paired.
5 The winner is the child with the most pairs.

Space fleet track game
Copymasters 117–119.
An activity for two children.

Objective of the activity
To provide practice of the **th**, **ch**, **wh**, and **sh** sounds in an exciting and repetitive activity.
You will need:
A dice.

Preparation
a) Photocopy the copymasters.
b) Colour and cut out all the pieces. Join the track using adhesive tape then cover all the pieces as explained in the General Instructions.

To use the activity
1 The letter tiles are mixed up and placed face downwards in a pile.
2 Each child throws the dice, the child with the highest score begins and play continues in a clockwise direction.
3 The first child shakes the dice and moves forward the number shown; when the pathways divide the child chooses which way to go. If he or she lands on a lettered square he or she picks up the top letter tile, if it completes the word on the lettered square the tile is placed on the track and the child collects a space ship. If the letter tile does not fit it is placed face upwards to form a 'used' pile.
4 The other children take their turns in the same way.
5 When the first pile of letter tiles has been used the 'used' stack is turned over and re-used.
6 The game continues until all the words have been completed.
7 The winner is the child with the largest space fleet.

Eskimos winter track game
Copymasters 122–124.
An activity for two children.

Objective of the activity
To provide practice in distinguishing between the **ir**, **er**, and **ur** blends (they all say er) in an exciting and repetitive activity.

Preparation and use
As for the 'Space fleet track game', though in this game the children collect fish not rockets.

Beach toys track game
Copymasters 127–129.
An activity for two–four children.

Objective of the activity
To provide practice in distinguishing between ll, ss, and ff in an exciting and repetitive activity.

Preparation and use
As for the 'Space fleet track game' but in this game the children collect beach toys.

The fishing game and fishing for ducks
Copymasters 133, 134 and 135
An activity for 1–6 children

Objective of the activity
To provide practice in reading the long vowel takes -ke and the short vowel takes ck rules.

You will need:
A cardboard box, paper clips, a horseshoe magnet and a piece of string. Each child will need a piece of paper and a pencil to record the score. The paper should be divided into two columns, one headed catch, the other fish or ducks that got away.

Preparation
a) Photocopy the required copymasters.
b) Colour, cut out and cover the fish or ducks as explained in the General Instructions.
c) A pond can be made using a cardboard box.
d) Tie the string onto the magnet to make a fishing line.
e) Slide the paper clips onto the fish or ducks so they will be attracted to the line.
f) Place the fish or ducks or both, into the pond.

To use the equipment
1 The child is given a set number of attempts to catch fish or ducks. If more than one child is playing, each child in turn tries to catch a fish or duck.
2 Any catch must be read correctly. If the word on the fish or duck is correctly read the child records the score (this being the number on the fish or duck). If the word is incorrectly read the fish or duck is recorded in the column for the one that got away. This should be done in pictorial form with the correct word written on the fish or duck.
3 If more than one child is playing the catch may be totalled to establish the winner.

Boys and girls come out to play
Copymasters 136–8.
An activity for a single child or a group of children.

You willl need:
A timer.

Objective of the activity
To build self-confidence by providing repetitive practice using a learnt rule.

Preparation
a) Photocopy the copymasters, one set for each child.
b) Join the base boards, then colour, cut out and cover all the pieces as explained in the General Instructions.

To use the activity
1 Each child's set of equipment consists of a base board, letter tiles and a rule card.
2 The timer is started and the children race to place their letters on their board to fill the spaces correctly and complete the words.
3 The first child to finish stops the timer and their answers are checked against the answer card. If all the letters have been correctly placed the child wins. If not, all boards are checked and the child with the highest number of correctly placed letter tiles is the winner.

Alphabet

a	b	c
d	e	f
g	h	i
j	k	l

Alphabet

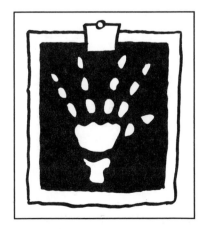

Alphabet

m	n	o
p	q	r
s	t	u
v	w	x

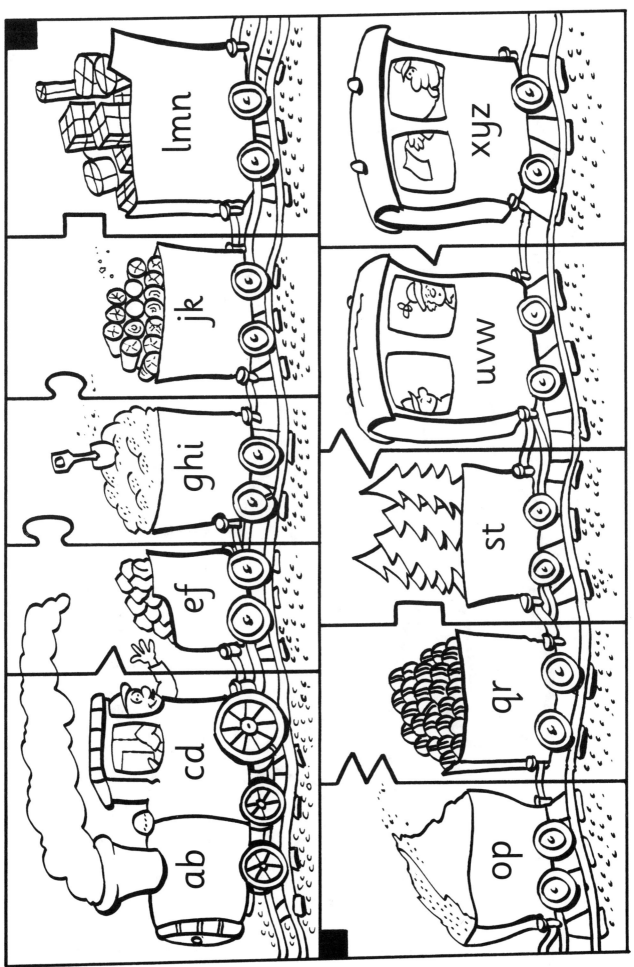

Build Kitty the Cat.

Alphabet

	f	f	f	
a	e	e	e	
	d	d	d	
	c	c	c	
	b	b	b	
	a	a	a	

Start

Help the frogs hop across the pond.

r	r	r
q	q	q
p	p	p
o	o	o
n	n	n
m	m	m
l	l	l
k	k	k
j	j	j
i	i	i
h	h	h
g	g	g

Alphabet

Copymaster 13

Frog race track game 3

Finish

z	z	z
y	y	y
x	x	x
w	w	w
v	v	v
u	u	u
t	t	t
s	s	s

Alphabet

Copymaster 14

a

b

c

d

e

f

g

h

i

j

k

l

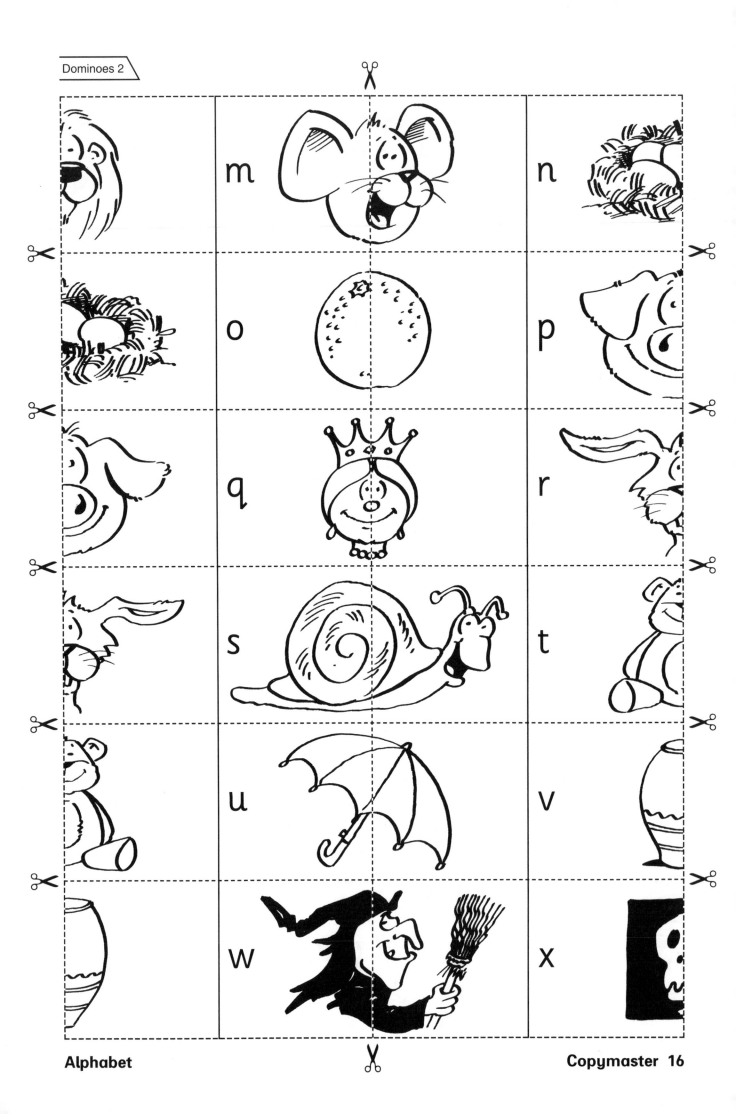

m

n

o

p

q

r

s

t

u

v

w

x

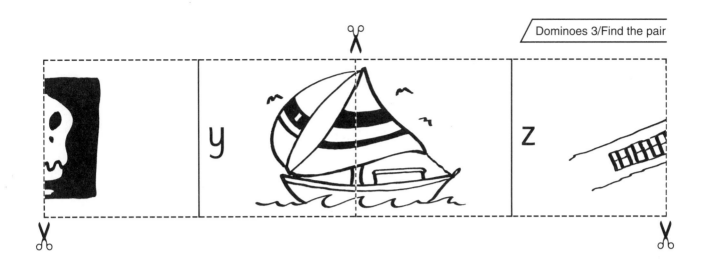

These 'Find the pair' pieces belong with Copymasters 1–4.

The alphabet

a	b	c	d
e	f	g	h
i	j	k	l
m	n	o	p
q	r	s	t
u	v	w	x
	y	z	

Alphabet

THE ALPHABET

A	B	C	D
E	F	G	H
I	J	K	L
M	N	O	P
Q	R	S	T
U	V	W	X
	Y	Z	

Alphabet   **Copymaster 19**

Z	a	A	b
B	c	C	d
D	e	E	f
F	g	G	h
H	i	I	j
J	k	K	l

L	m	M	n
N	o	O	p
P	q	Q	r
R	s	S	t
T	u	U	v
V	w	W	x

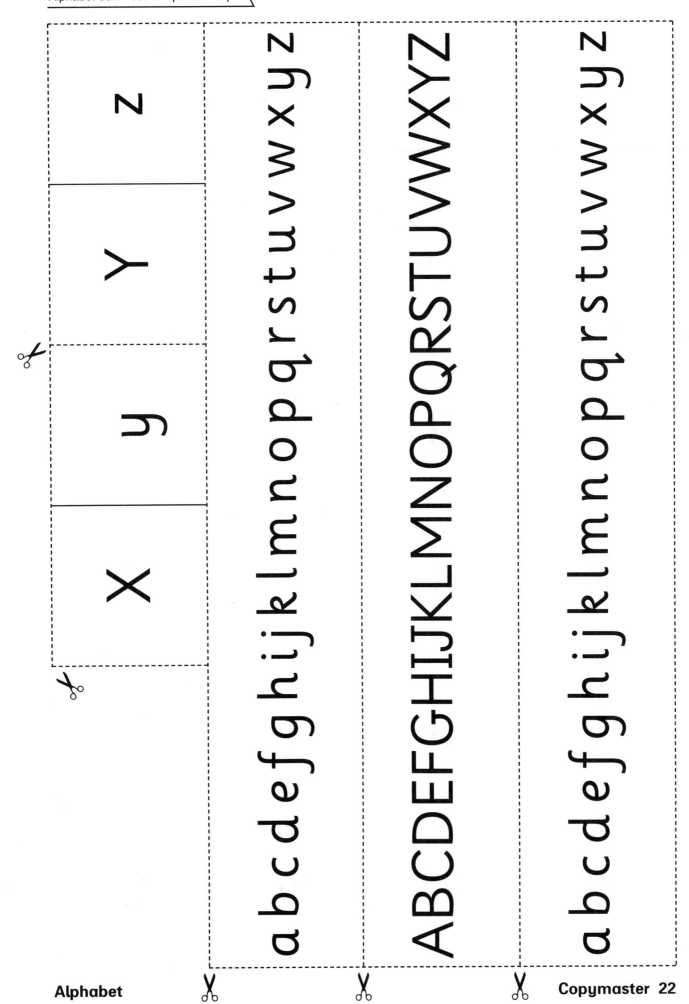

X Y Z

x y z

a b c d e f g h i j k l m n o p q r s t u v w x y z

A B C D E F G H I J K L M N O P Q R S T U V W X Y Z

a b c d e f g h i j k l m n o p q r s t u v w x y z

a 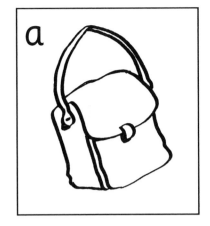   a 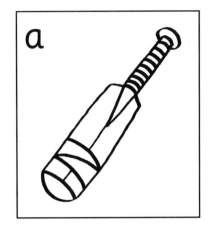   a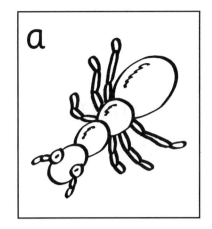

a    a    a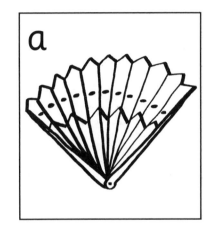

a 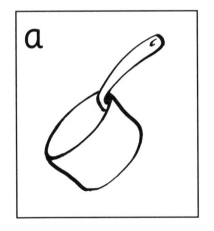   a    a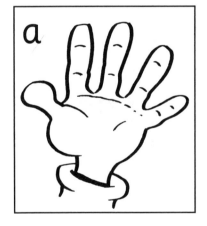

a    a    a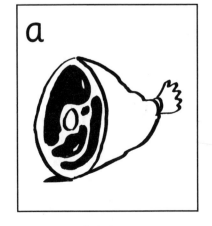

Short vowels   **Copymaster 23**

a	a	a
bag	bat	ant

a	a	a
jam	hat	fan

a	a	a
pan	cat	hand

a	a	a
lamp	rabbit	ham

Short vowels

Short vowels

Copymaster 25

a	i	u
The vowels	e	o

a	i	u
The vowels	e	o

i

i

i

i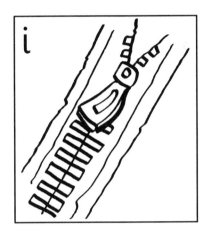

i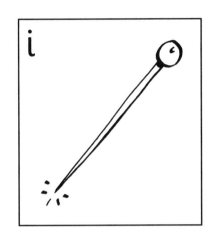

i

i

i

i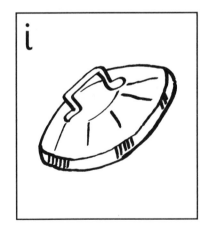

i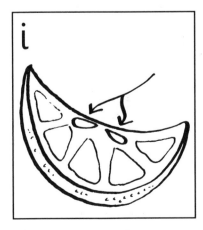

i

i

Short vowels

Copymaster 27

i	i	i
pig	tins	king

i	i	i
zip	pin	ring

i	i	i
mill	milk	lid

i	i	i
pips	bin	fish

Short vowels

pig	i	king	i
tins	i	pin	i
ring	i	milk	i
zip	i	mill	i
lid	i	bin	i
fish	i	pips	i

net	*e*	hen	*e*
teddy	*e*	web	*e*
red	*e*	ten	*e*
bell	*e*	tent	*e*
bed	*e*	elf	*e*
leg	*e*	egg	*e*

e

e

e

e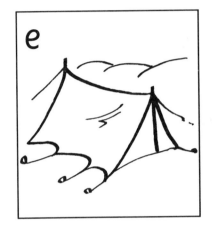

e

e

e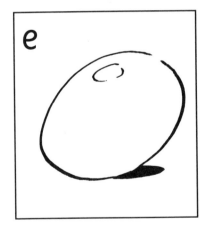

e

e

e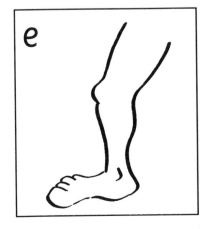

e

e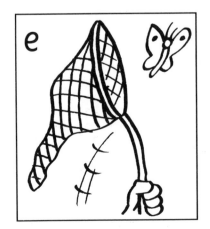

Short vowels

Copymaster 31

e

bed

e

red

e

bell

e

tent

e

web

e

ten

e

egg

e

hen

e

teddy

e

leg

e

elf

e

net

Short vowels

O

O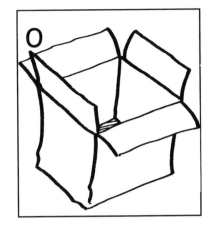

O

O

O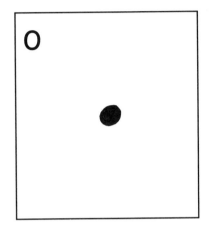

O

O

O

O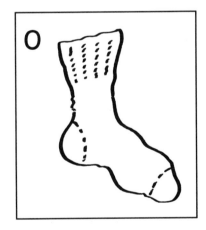

O

O

O

Short vowels

Copymaster 33

o pot	o box	o frog
o dog	o dot	o fox
o cot	o holly	o sock
o lock	o clock	o bomb

Short vowels

u 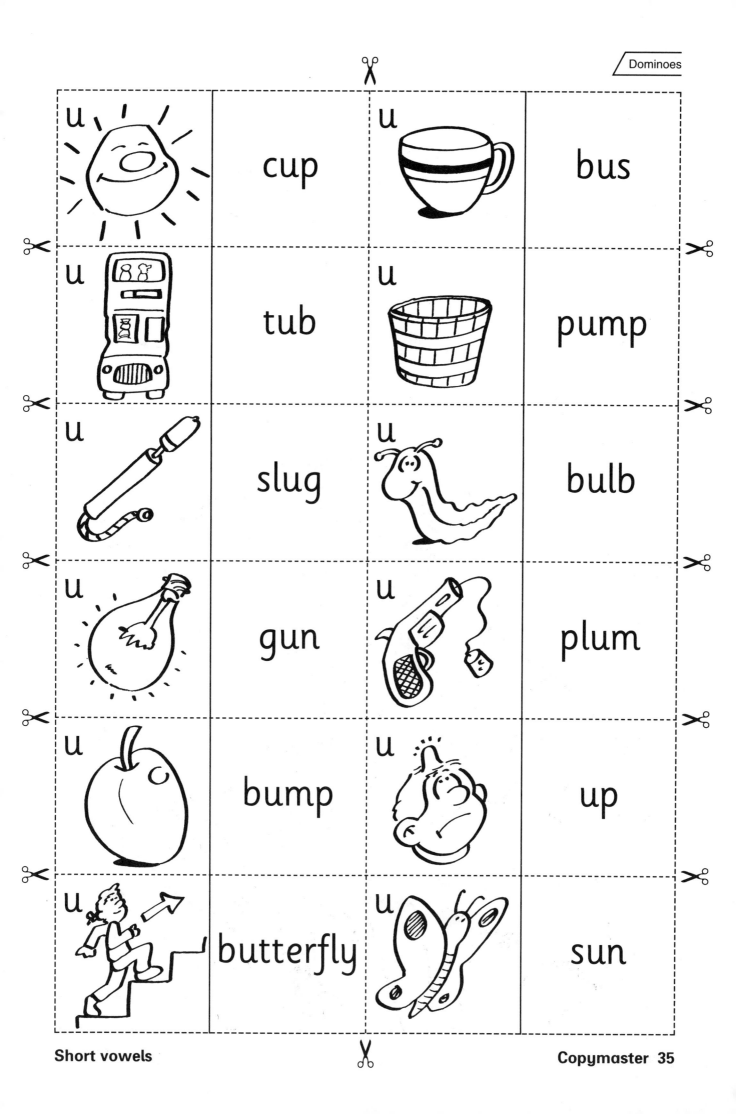	cup	u	bus
u	tub	u	pump
u	slug	u	bulb
u	gun	u	plum
u	bump	u	up
u	butterfly	u	sun

Short vowels

Short vowels

Short vowels

Short vowels

d _ d

b _ d

t _ n

d _ g

r _ d

l _ g

l _ d

Short vowels

u	u	u	u
u	u	u	u
a	e	i	o
a	e	i	o
a	e	i	o
a	e	i	o
a	e	i	o
a	e	i	o
a	e	i	o
a	e	i	o

Short vowels   **Copymaster 42**

eep

ipper

ug

sl

sl

sl

edge

eeve

ide

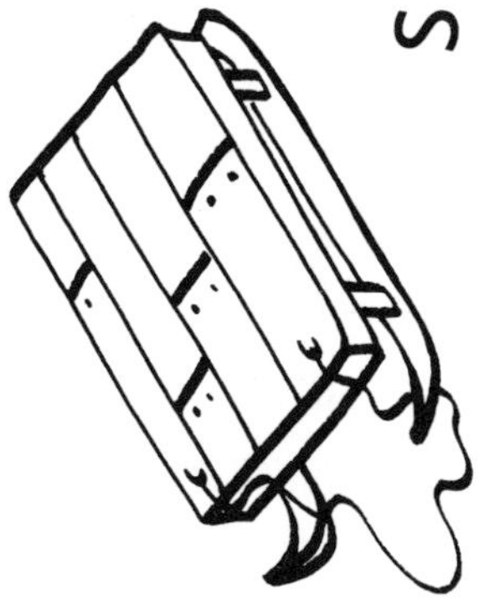

sl

sl

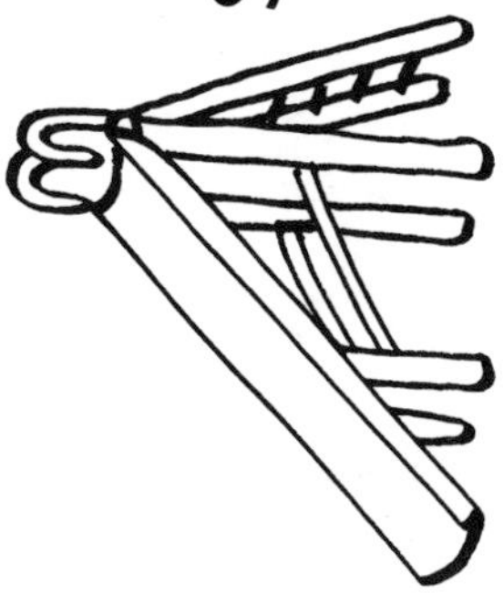

sl

Initial blends

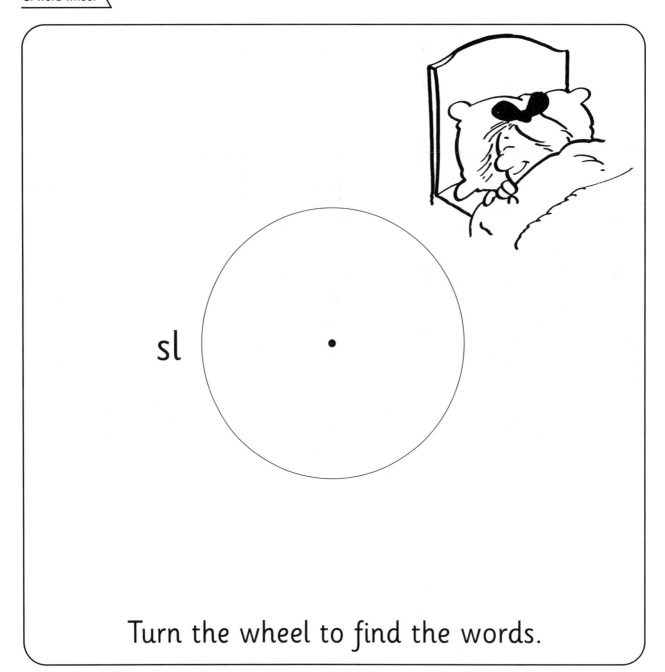

sl

Turn the wheel to find the words.

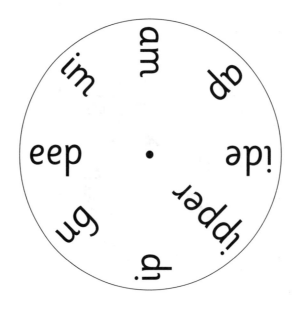

Initial blends

Copymaster 44

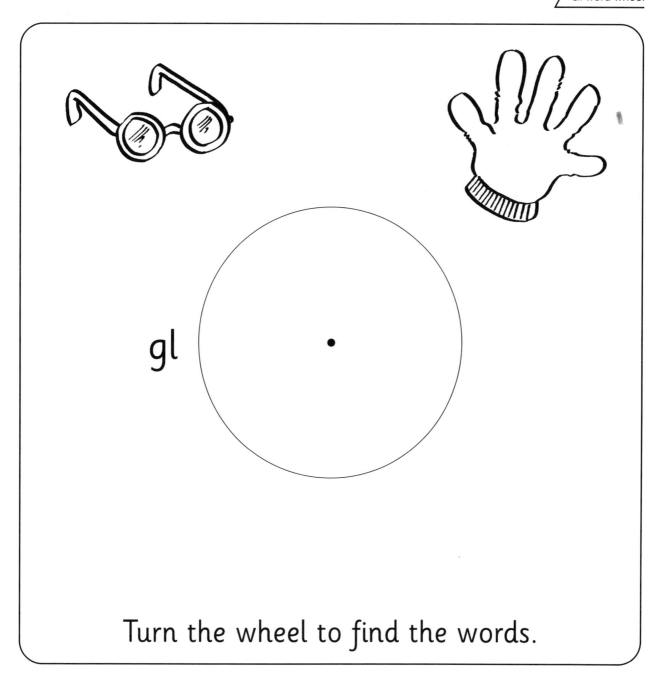

gl

Turn the wheel to find the words.

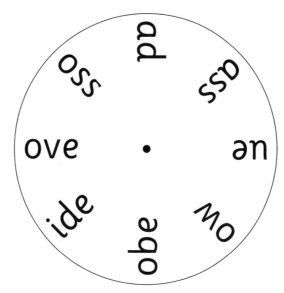

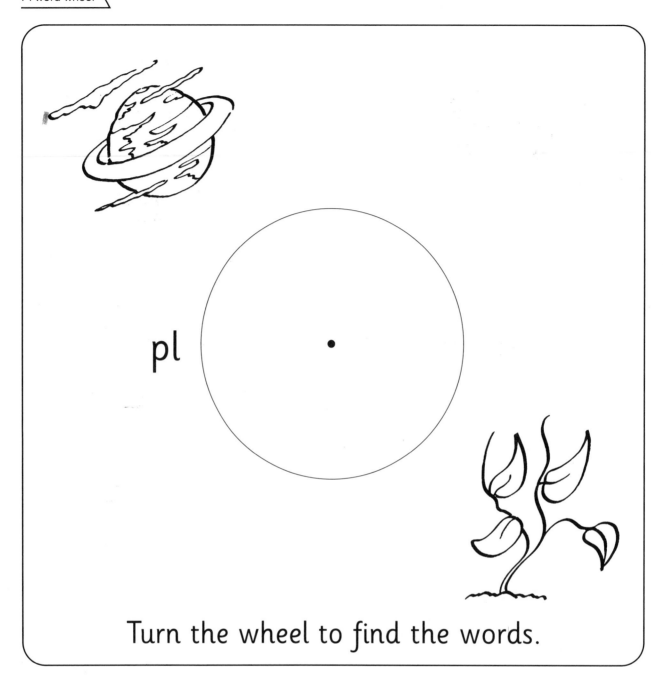

pl

Turn the wheel to find the words.

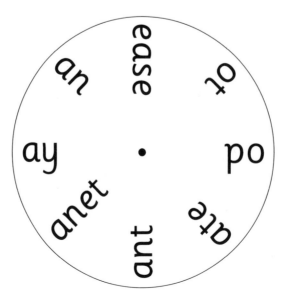

Initial blends

cr	gr	fl
st	cl	pl
bl	gl	tr

Fill the board

idge	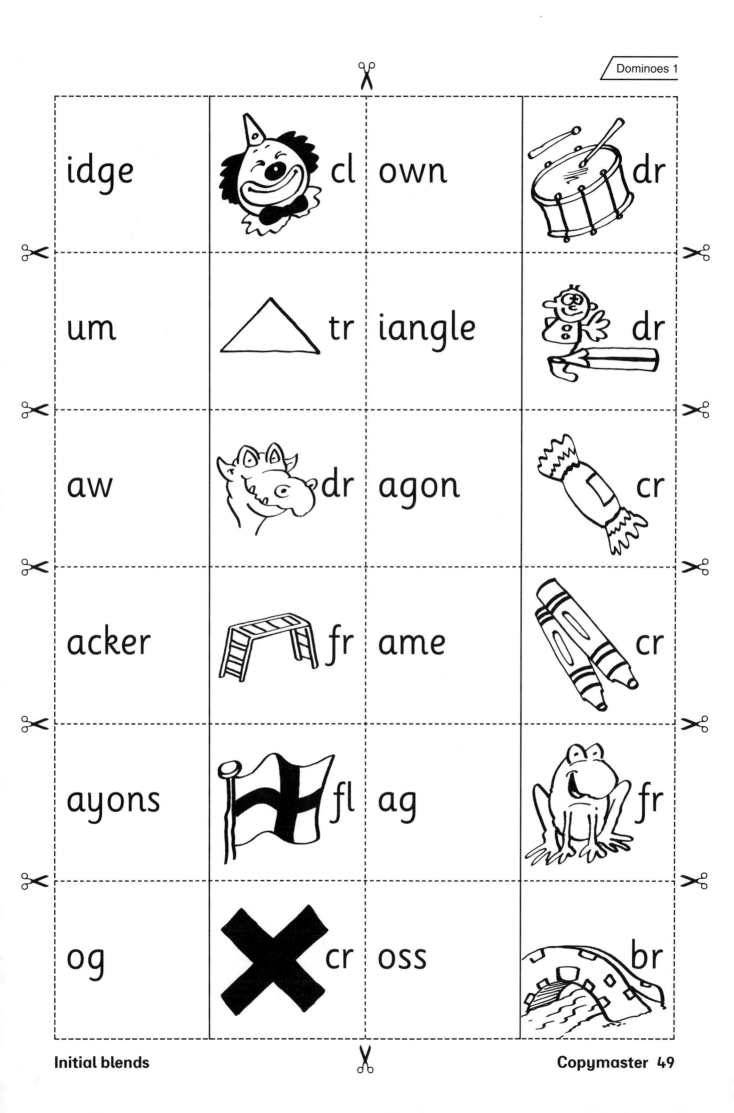cl	own	dr
um	tr	iangle	dr
aw	dr	agon	cr
acker	fr	ame	cr
ayons	fl	ag	fr
og	cr	oss	br

ower	 cl	ock	 gl
ove	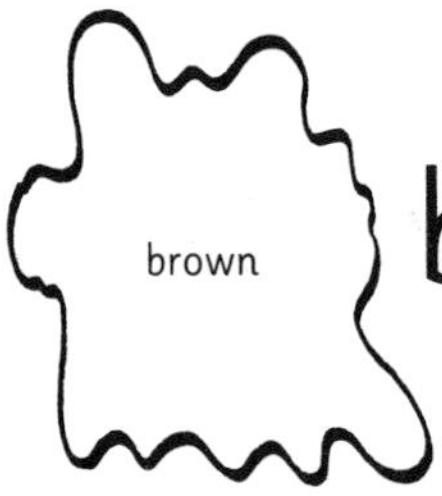 br	own	 sl
ipper	 tr	ain	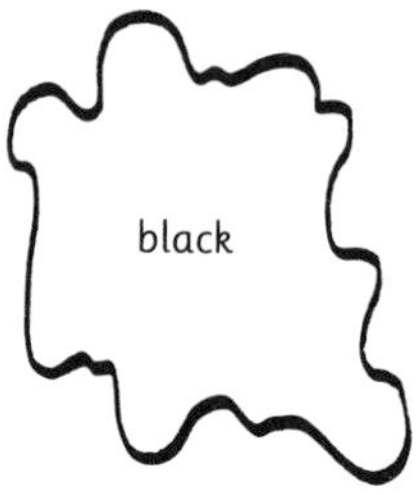 bl
ack	 sn	owman	 tr
ee	 sl	eep	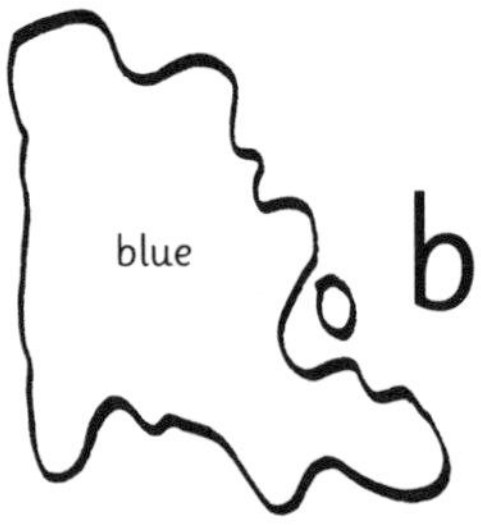 bl
ue	 br	ick	 fl

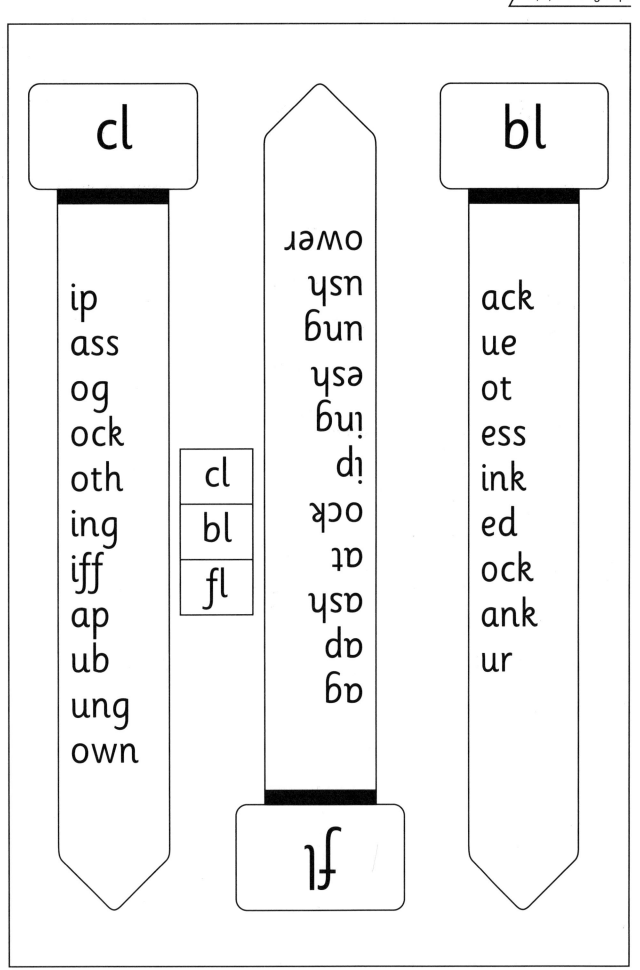

cl

ip
ass
og
ock
oth
ing
iff
ap
ub
ung
own

cl
bl
fl

bl

ack
ue
ot
ess
ink
ed
ock
ank
ur

ower
ush
ung
esh
ing
ip
ock
at
ash
ap
ag

fl

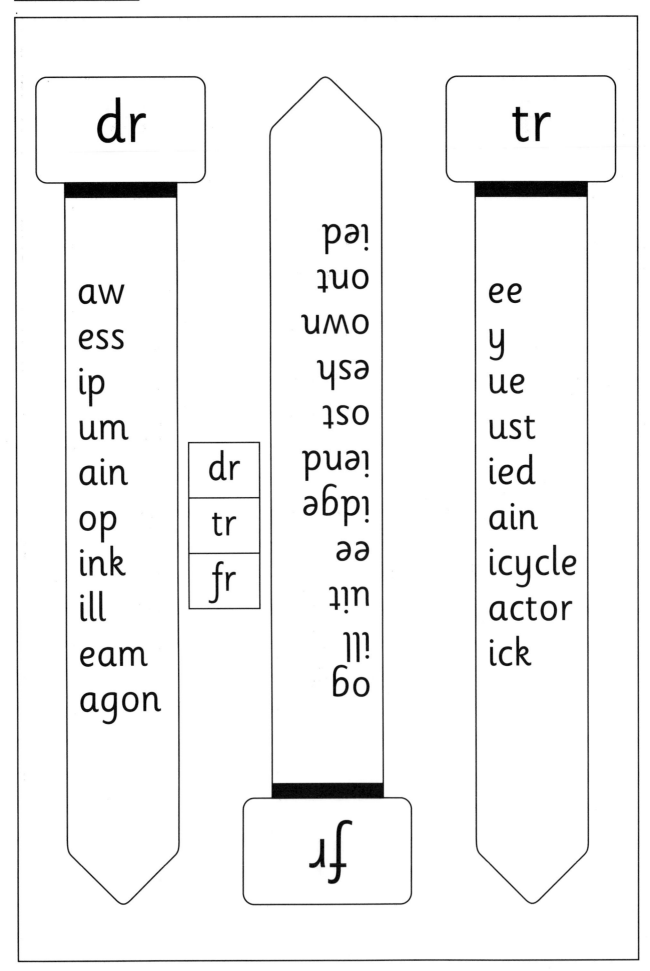

dr

aw
ess
ip
um
ain
op
ink
ill
eam
agon

| dr |
| tr |
| fr |

fr

ied
ont
own
esh
ost
iend
idge
ee
uit
ill
og

tr

ee
y
ue
ust
ied
ain
icycle
actor
ick

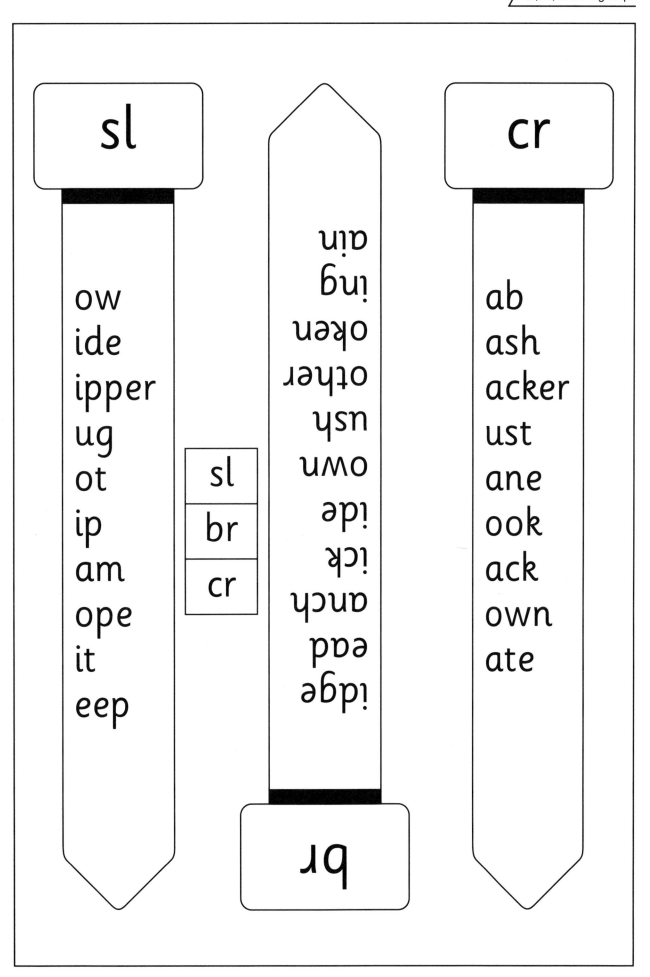

sl

ow
ide
ipper
ug
ot
ip
am
ope
it
eep

cr

ab
ash
acker
ust
ane
ook
ack
own
ate

| sl |
| br |
| cr |

ain
ing
oken
other
ush
own
ide
ick
anch
ead
idge

br

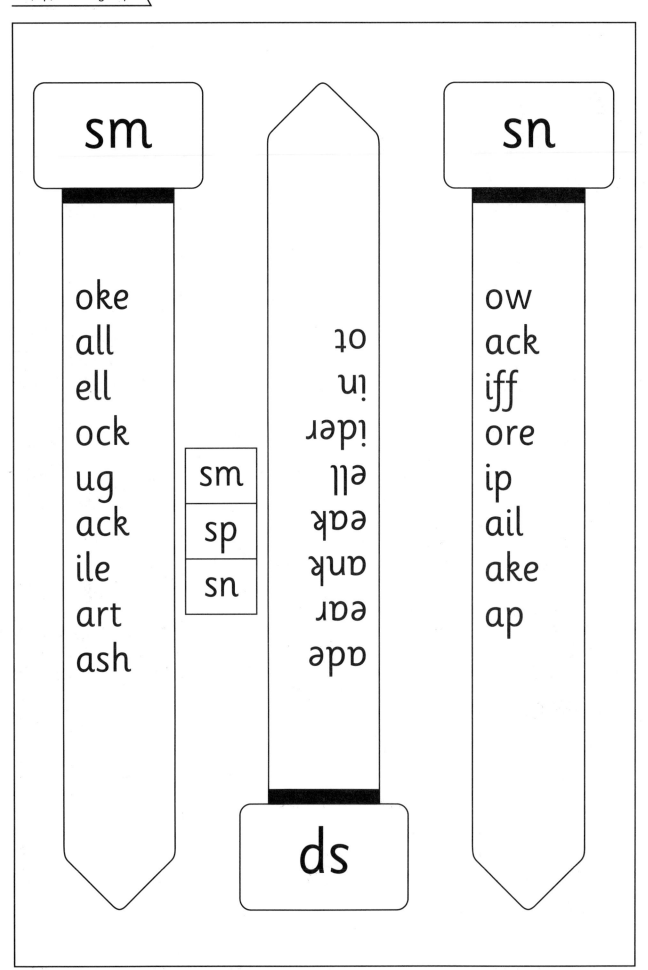

sm

oke
all
ell
ock
ug
ack
ile
art
ash

sn

ow
ack
iff
ore
ip
ail
ake
ap

| sm |
| sp |
| sn |

ot
in
ider
ell
eak
ank
ear
ade

sp

Initial blends

Name _____

Write the words on Sam's helmet.

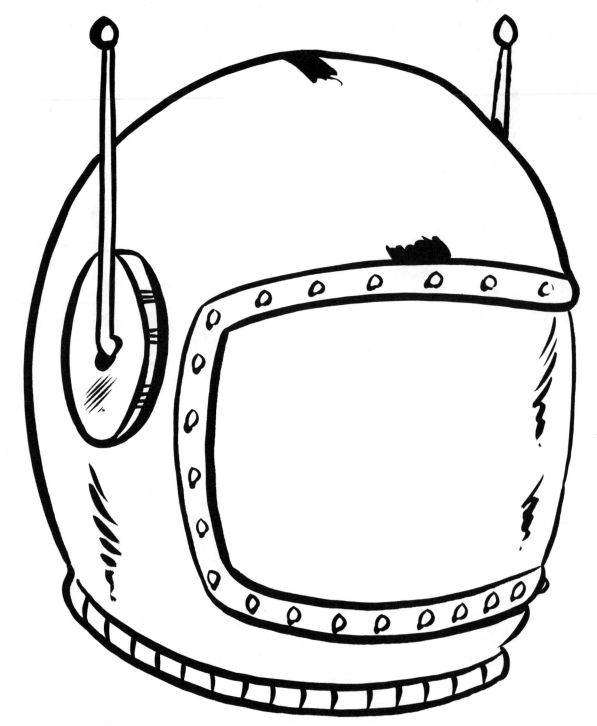

Use three of the words in sentences.

1 _____

2 _____

3 _____

Help Toby to find the words.

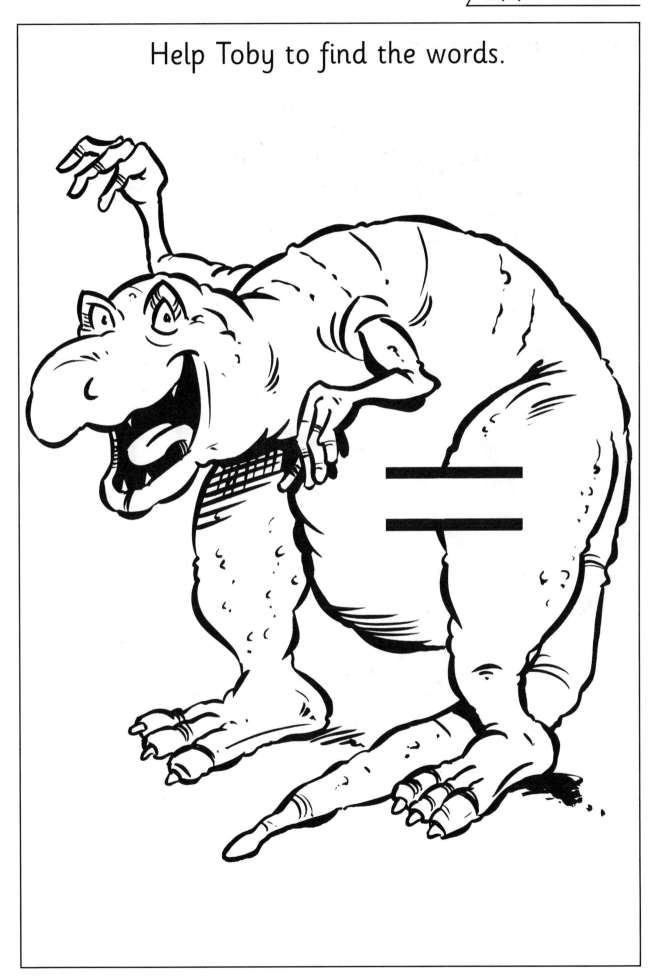

Name _____

Write the words you find on Toby.

Write three sentences using some of the words.

1 _____

2 _____

3 _____

Wordal

Name _____

t   x   a
                      c
   w   k   z
      d   s
o   q
                        u
i   g   v

r

b   Help Wordal find his words.
                 Write them here.
h

j

f   p

   e   y
m

Now use the words in sentences.

Remember to use capital letters and
full stops.

1 _____

2 _____

3 _____

Help Teddy to find the words.

Initial blends

Name _____

Find the words and write them here.

_____   _____

_____   _____

_____   _____

_____   _____

_____

_____

_____

Draw a teddy bears' picnic on the back of the page.

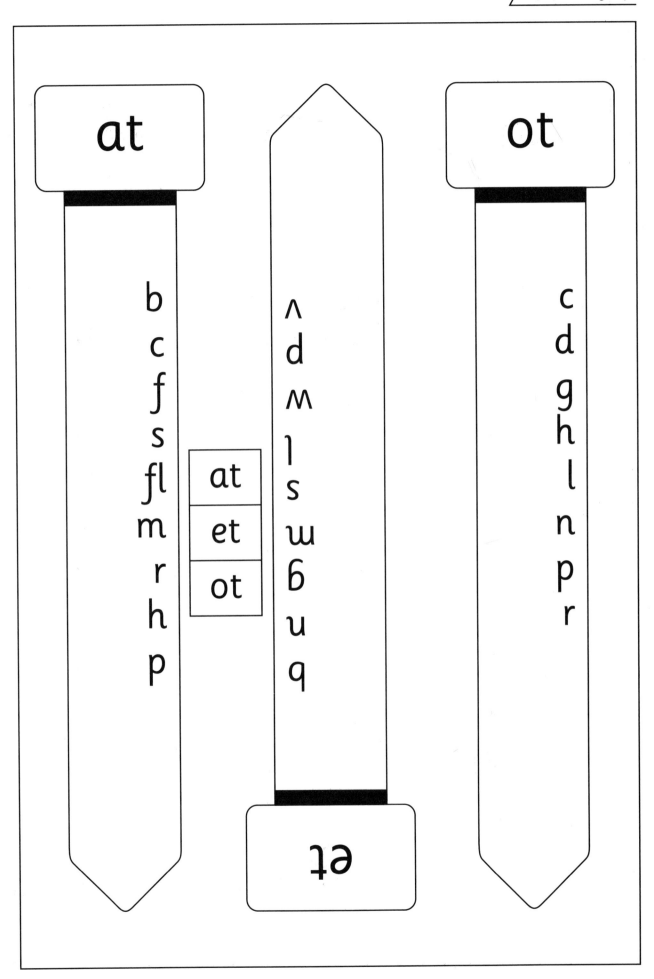

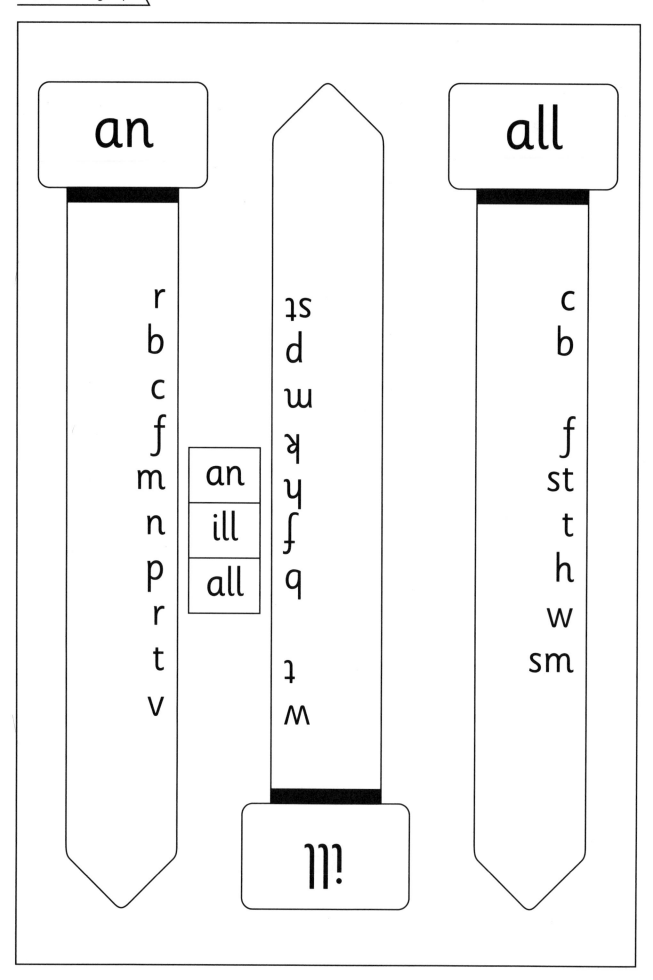

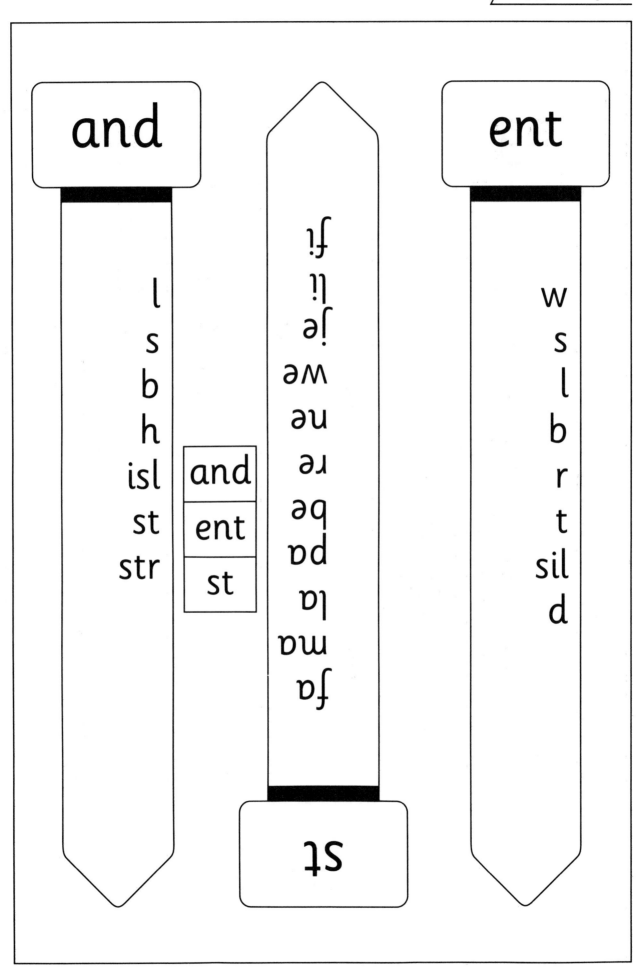

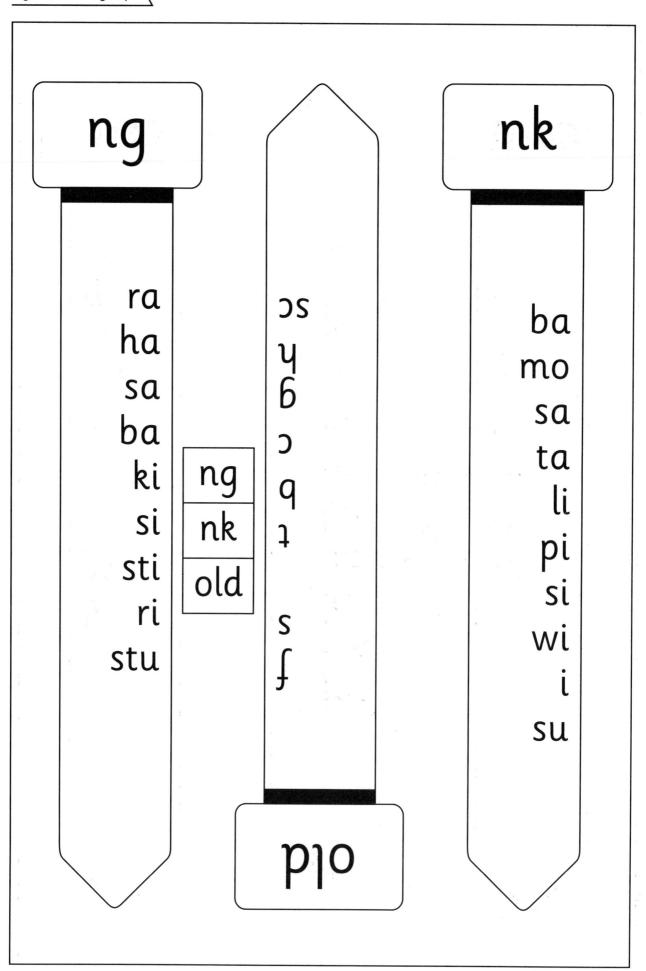

ng

ra
ha
sa
ba
ki
si
sti
ri
stu

ng
nk
old

sc
y
g
c
b
d
t
s
f

old

nk

ba
mo
sa
ta
li
pi
si
wi
i
su

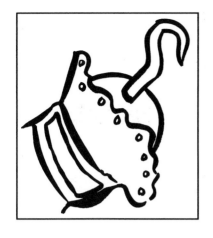

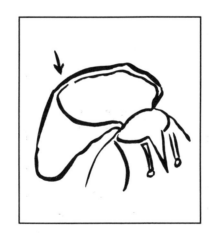

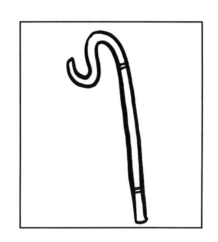

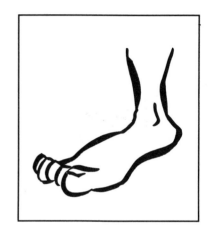

Long vowels

Copymaster 67

hook	cook	book
look	crook	foot
wool	hood	brook
rook	stood	wood

roots	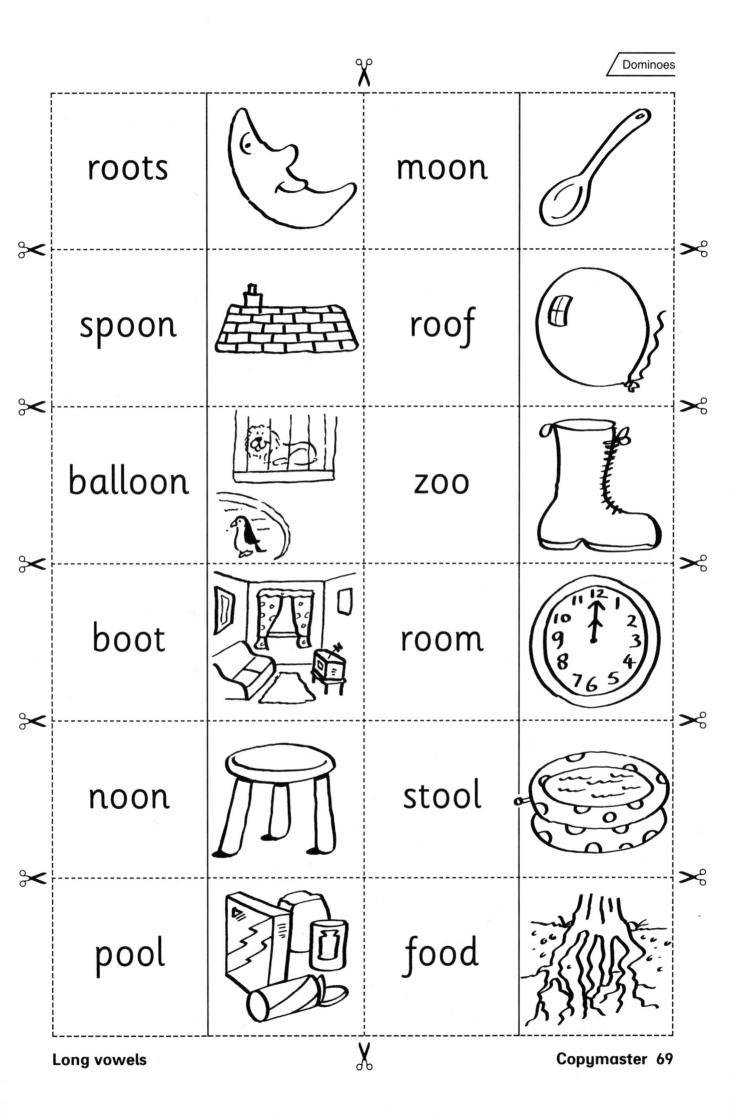	moon	
spoon		roof	
balloon		zoo	
boot		room	
noon		stool	
pool		food	

Long vowels

Long vowels

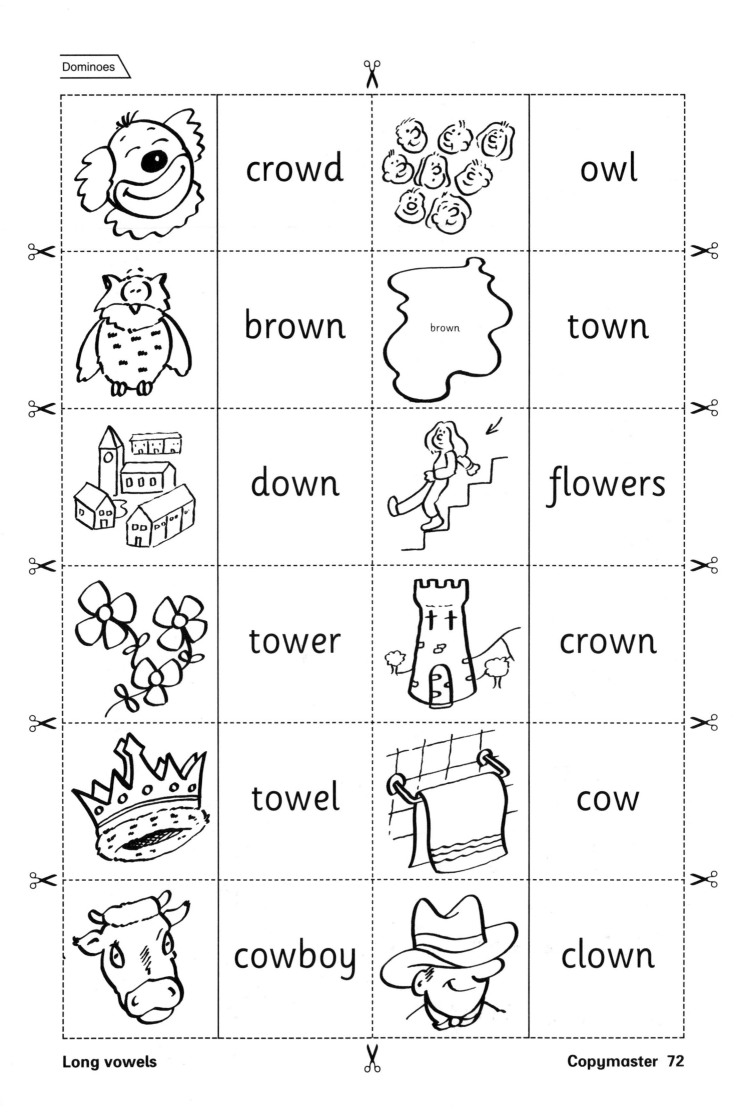

	crowd		owl
	brown		town
	down		flowers
	tower		crown
	towel		cow
	cowboy		clown

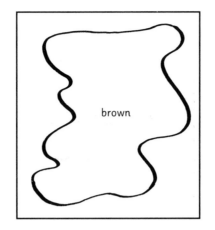

Long vowels

Copymaster 73

owl	brown	town
down	flowers	tower
crown	towel	cow
cowboy	clown	crowd

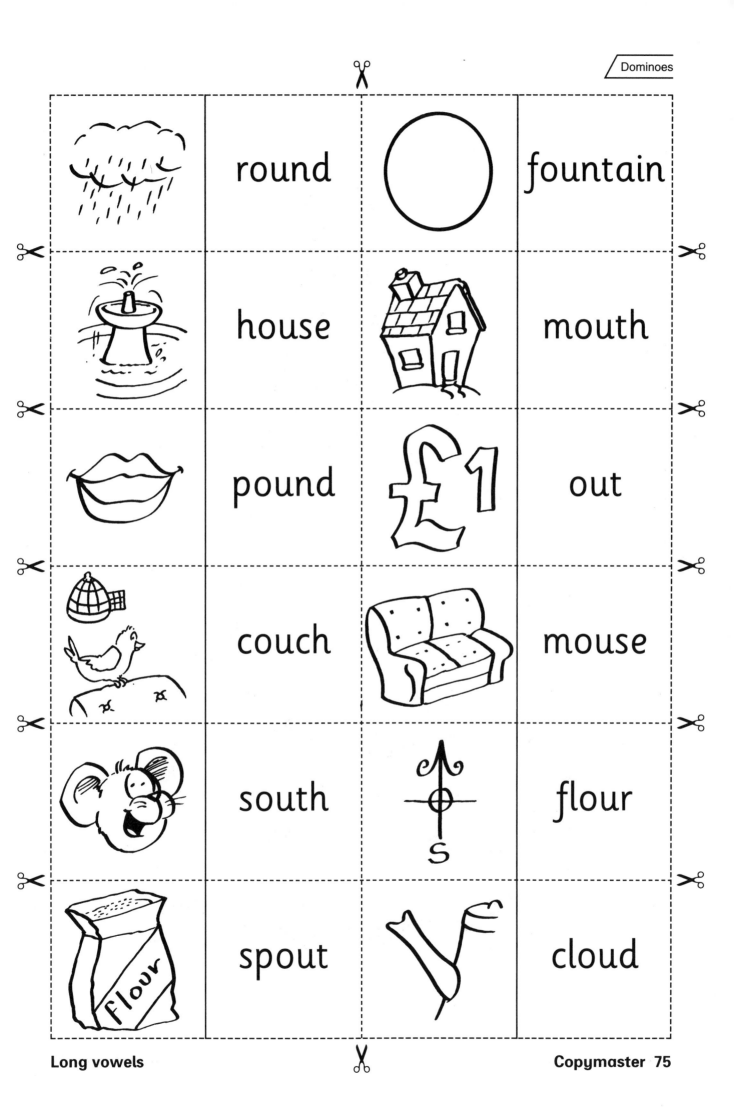	round	◯	fountain
	house		mouth
	pound	£1	out
	couch		mouse
	south	↑ S	flour
	spout		cloud

Long vowels   **Copymaster 75**

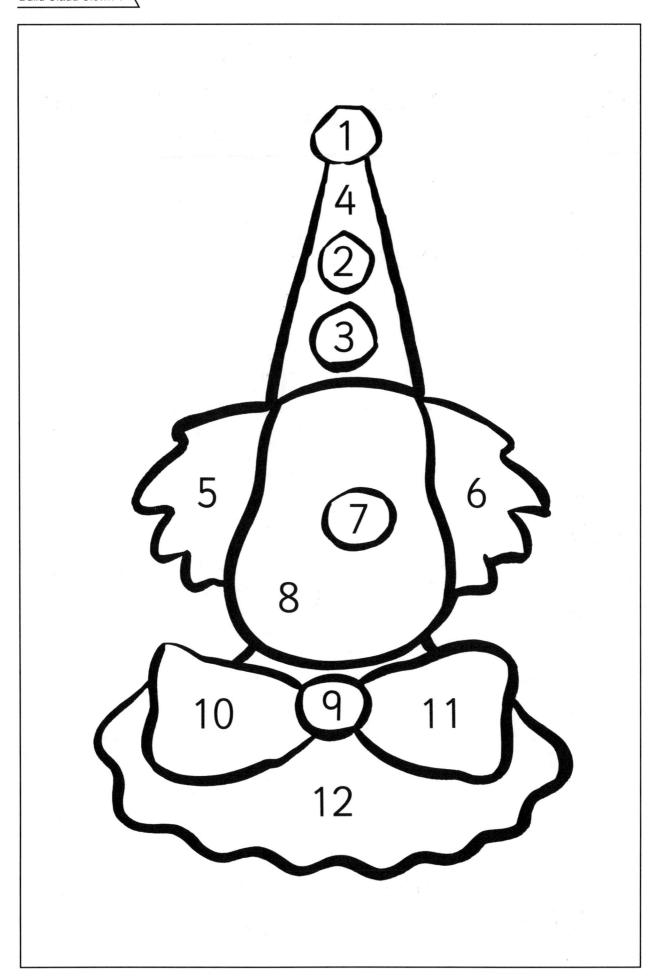

Long vowels

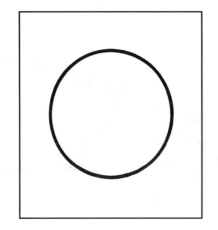

Long vowels

cloud	round	fountain
house	mouth	pound
out	couch	mouse
south	flour	spout

Long vowels

baker	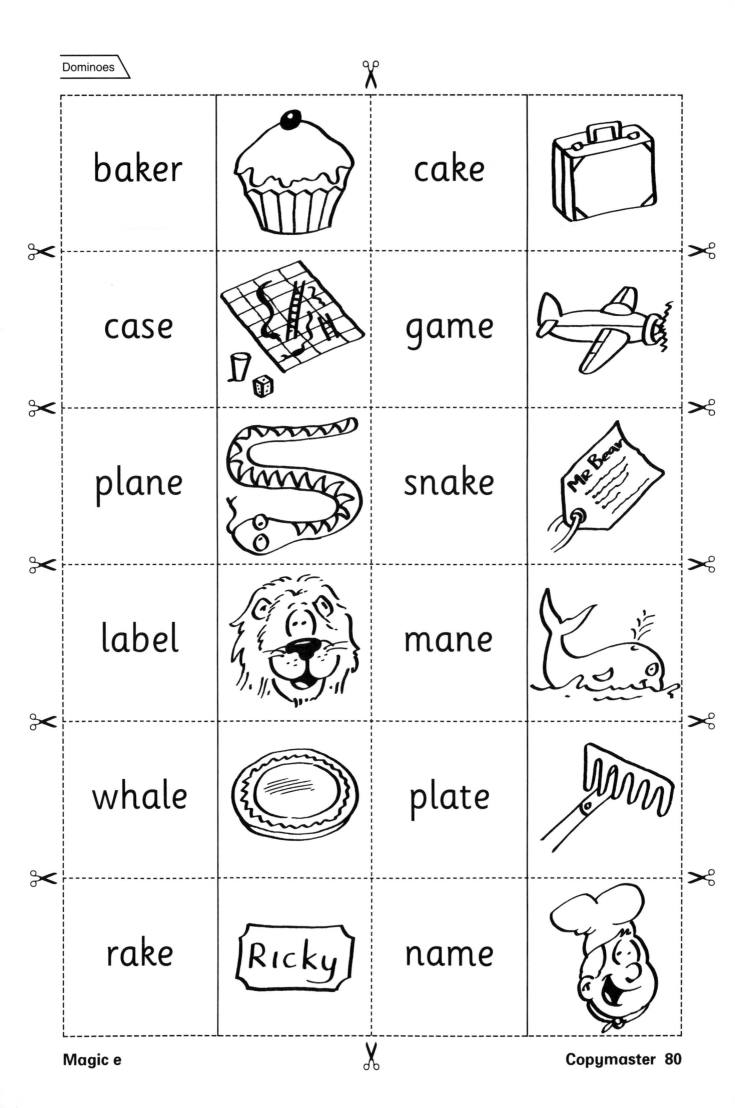	cake	
case		game	
plane		snake	
label		mane	
whale		plate	
rake		name	

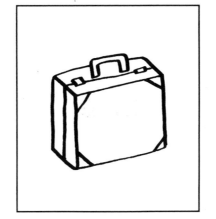

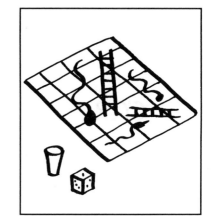

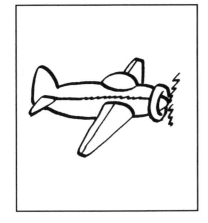

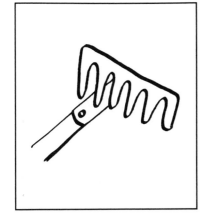

Alison
Paul
Ricky
Alastair
Alex

Magic e

cake	case	game
plane	snake	label
mane	whale	plate
rake	names	baker

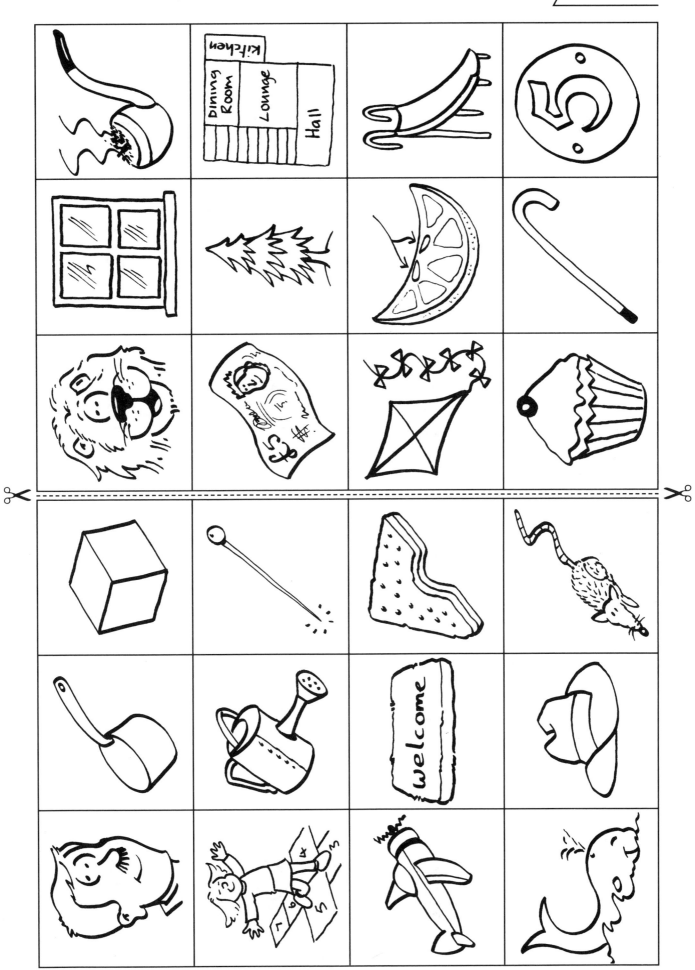

Magic e

pipe	pane	mane
plan	pine	note
slide	pip	kite
five	cane	cake

✂ - ✂

cube	pan	man
pin	can	hop
bite	mat	plane
rat	hat	whale

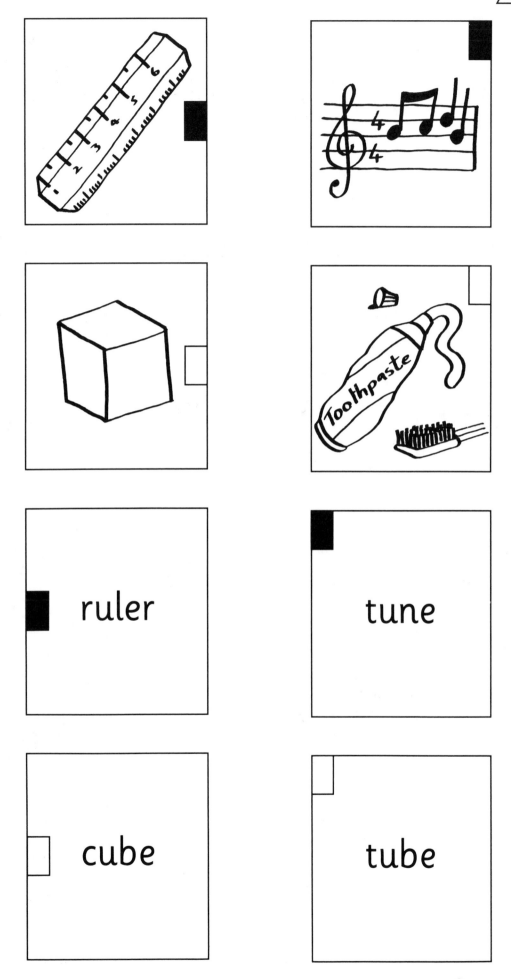

ruler

tune

cube

tube

Magic e

price	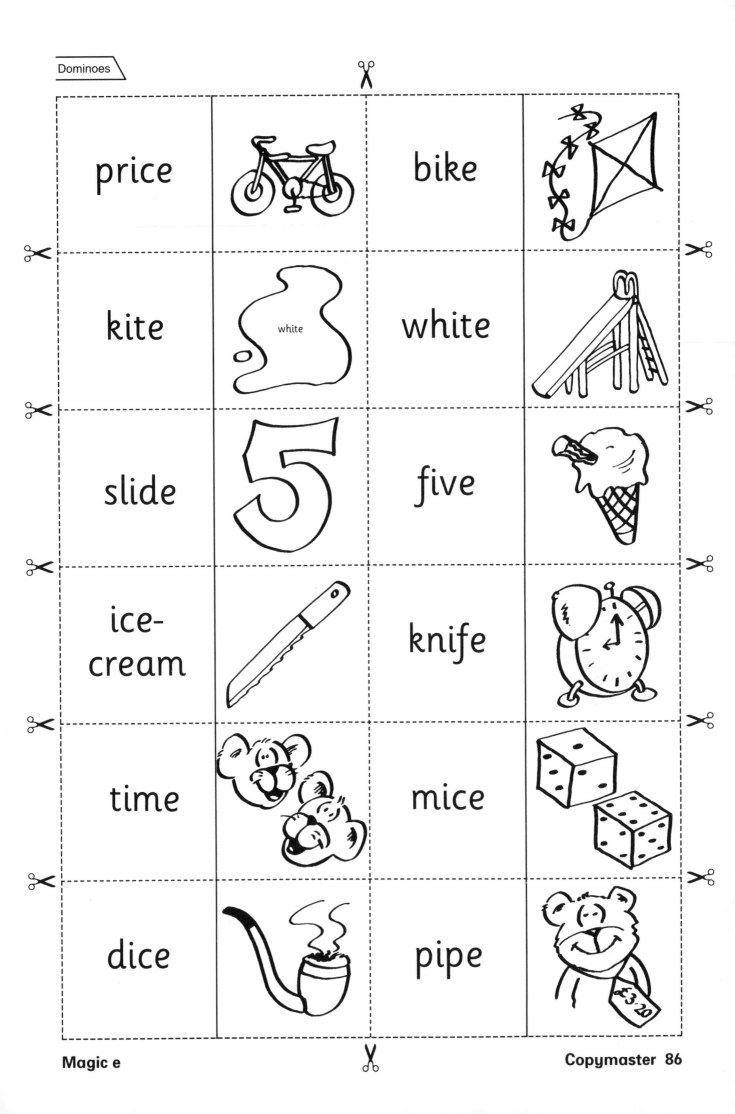	bike	
kite		white	
slide		five	
ice-cream		knife	
time		mice	
dice		pipe	

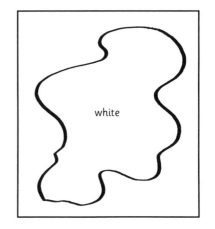

white

Magic e

bike	kite	white
time	five	ice-cream
knife	slide	mice
dice	pipe	price

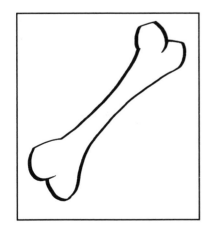

Magic e

tadpole	rose	stove
rope	hole	nose
smoke	coke	globe
bone	telephone	cone

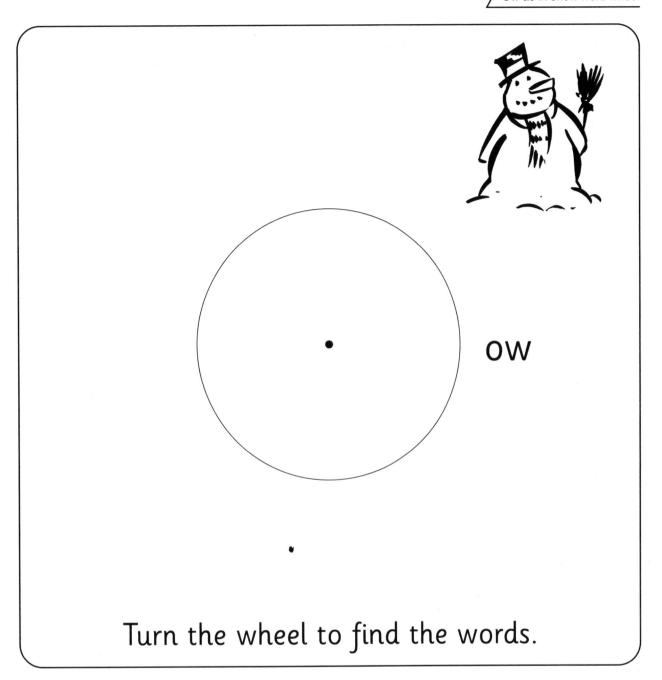

ow

Turn the wheel to find the words.

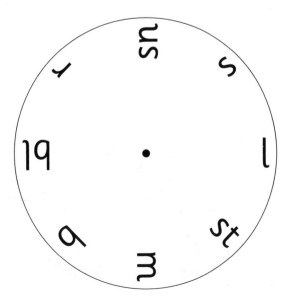

More long vowels

More long vowels

boat	road	toadstool
coat	goat	moat
float	foal	coach
throat	coal	goal

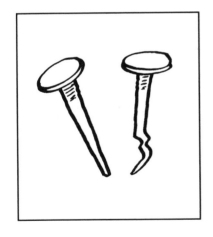

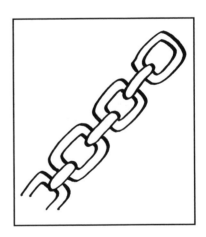

More long vowels

Copymaster 95

snail	sailor	paints
rain	train	sail
nails	tail	chain
daisy	rail	mermaid

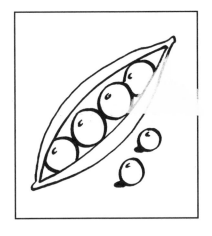  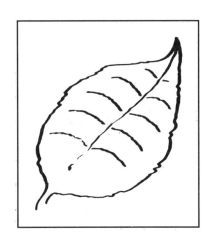

More long vowels

peas	meat	teapot
beans	sea	leaf
seal	beach	jeans
bead	lead	leak

More long vowels

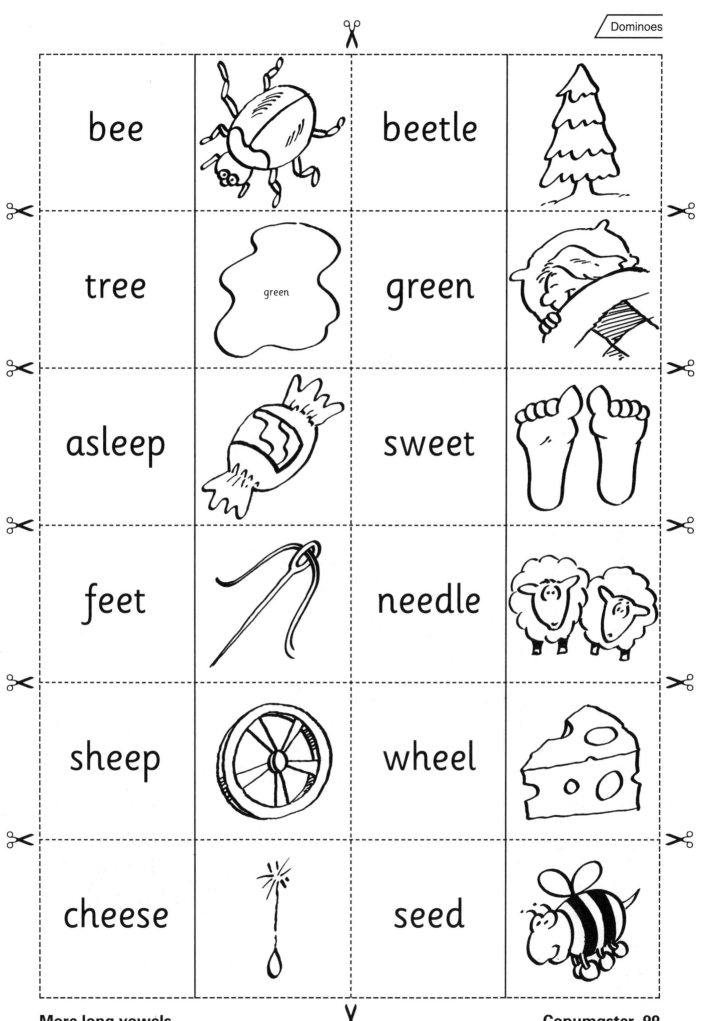

bee		beetle	
tree	green	green	
asleep		sweet	
feet		needle	
sheep		wheel	
cheese		seed	

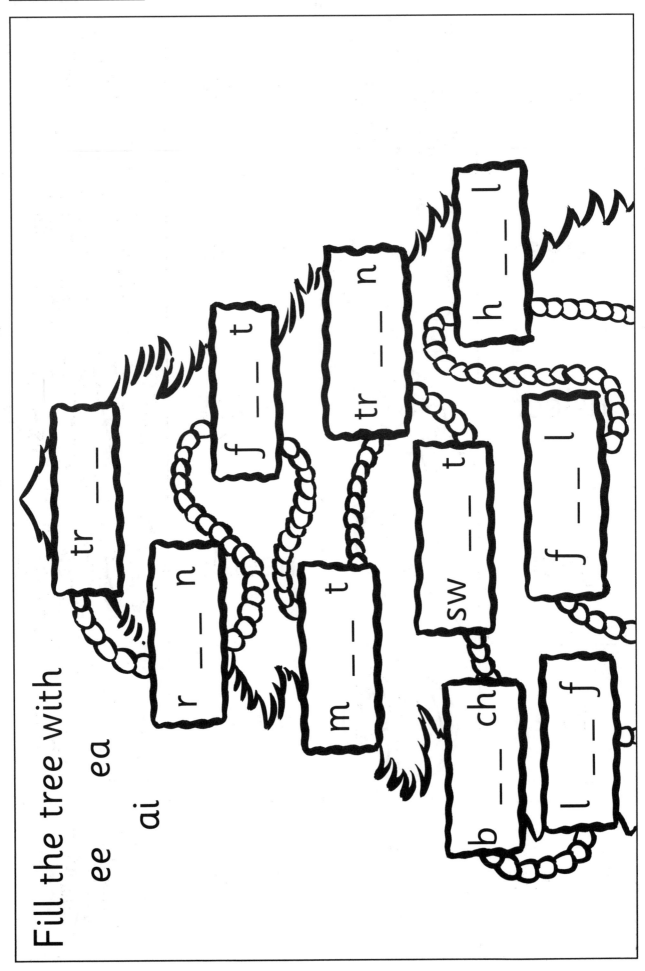

Fill the tree with

ee   ea

ai

The boxes on the tree contain:

tr _ _

f _ t

tr _ _ n

h _ _ l

r _ _ n

m _ _ t

sw _ _ t

f _ _ l

b _ _ ch

f _ _ l

More long vowels

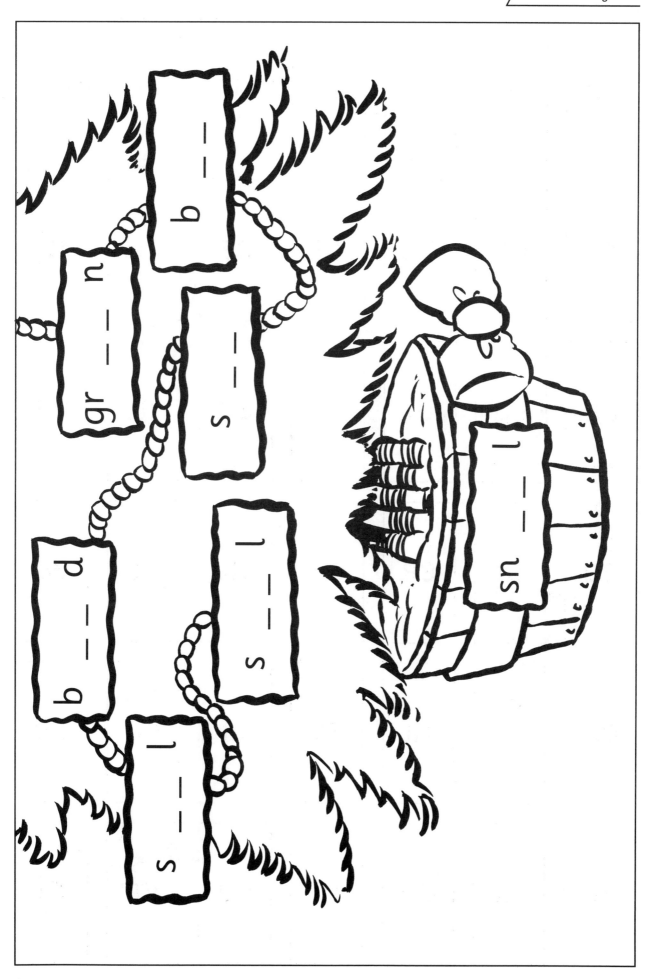

More long vowels

ea	ai	ee	ea	ai	ee	ea
ai	ee	ea	ai	ee	ea	ai
ee	ea	ai	ee	ea	ai	ee
ea	ai	ee	ea	ai	ee	ea
ea	ee	ai	ee	ai	ea	ee
ee	ai	ea	ai	ea	ee	ai

More long vowels

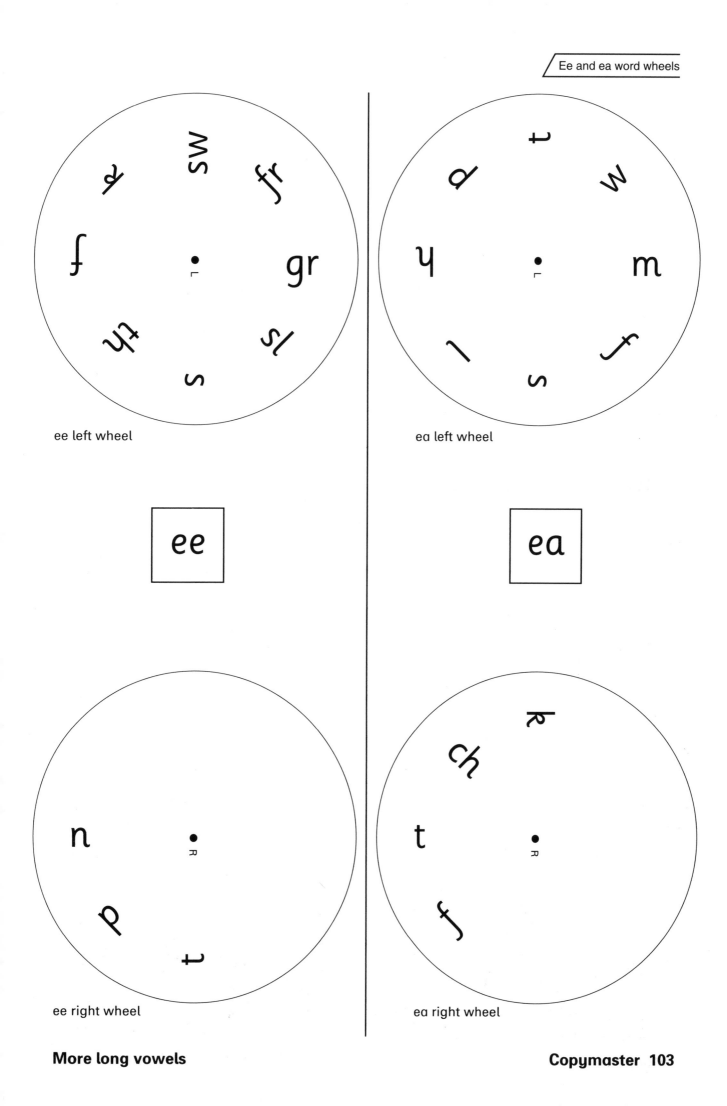

ee left wheel

ee

ee right wheel

ea left wheel

ea

ea right wheel

More long vowels

More long vowels

More long vowels

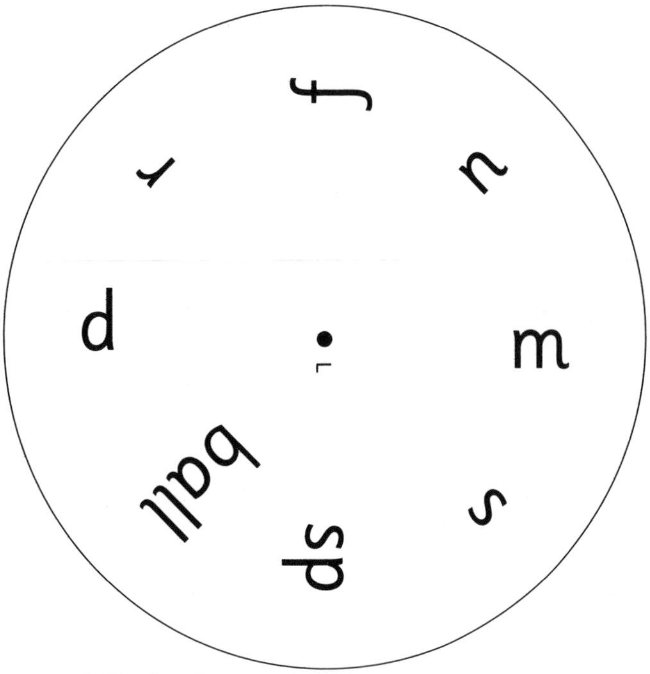

oo left wheel

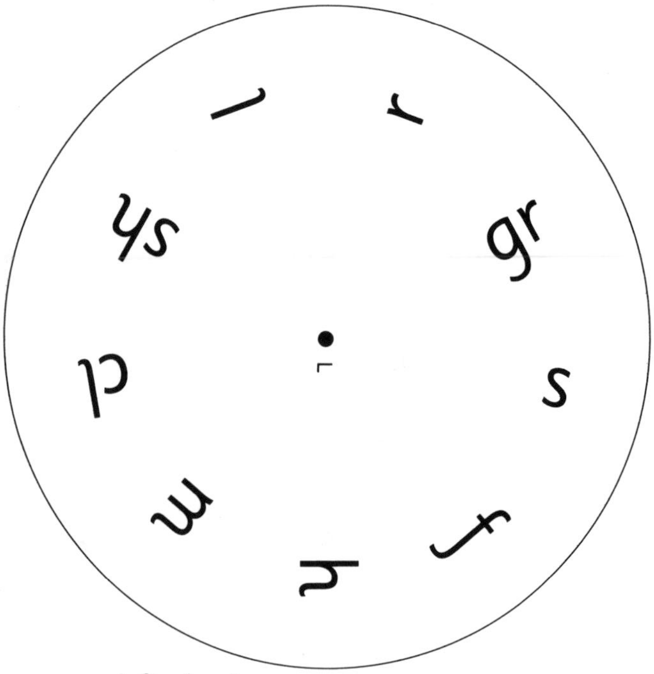

ou left wheel

oo

ou

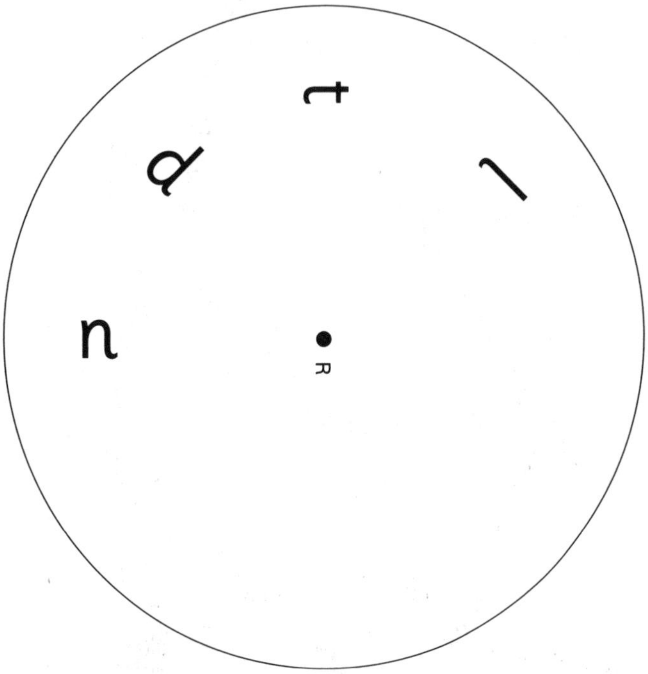

oo right wheel

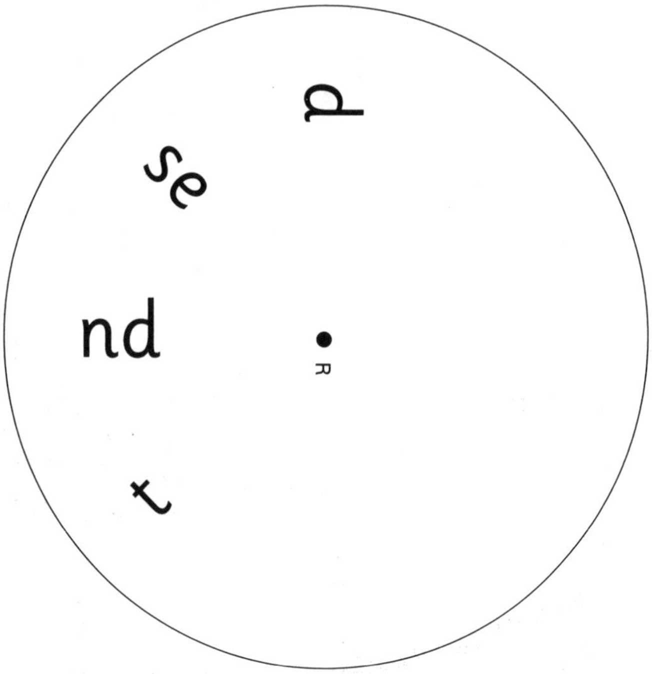

ou right wheel

More long vowels

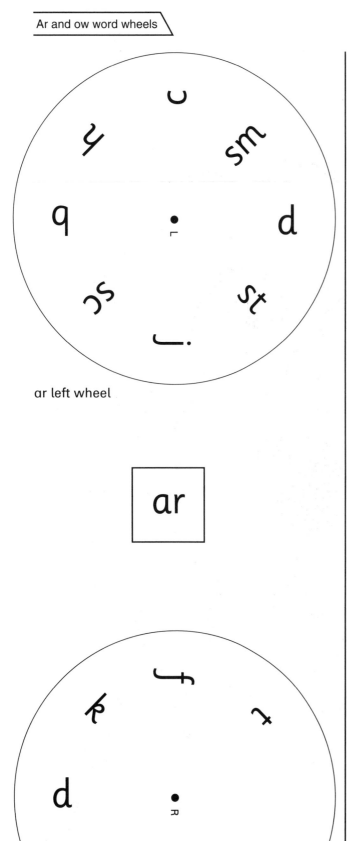

ar left wheel

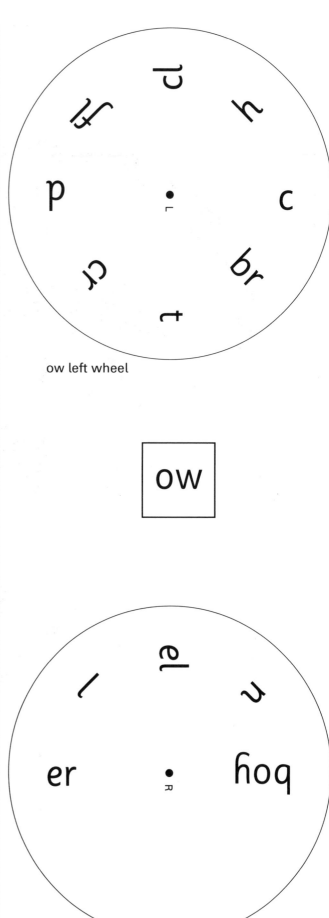

ow left wheel

ar

ow

ar right wheel

ow right wheel

More long vowels

Write the words on Leo's mane.

Write three sentences using some of the words you have found.

1 _____

2 _____

3 _____

Now draw a lion.

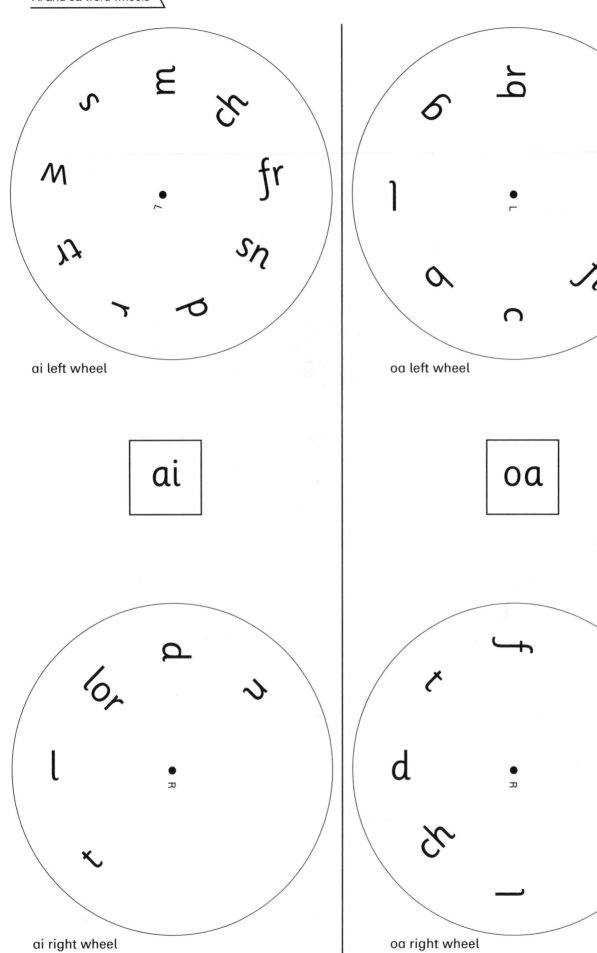

ai left wheel

oa left wheel

ai

oa

ai right wheel

oa right wheel

More long vowels

Copymaster 110

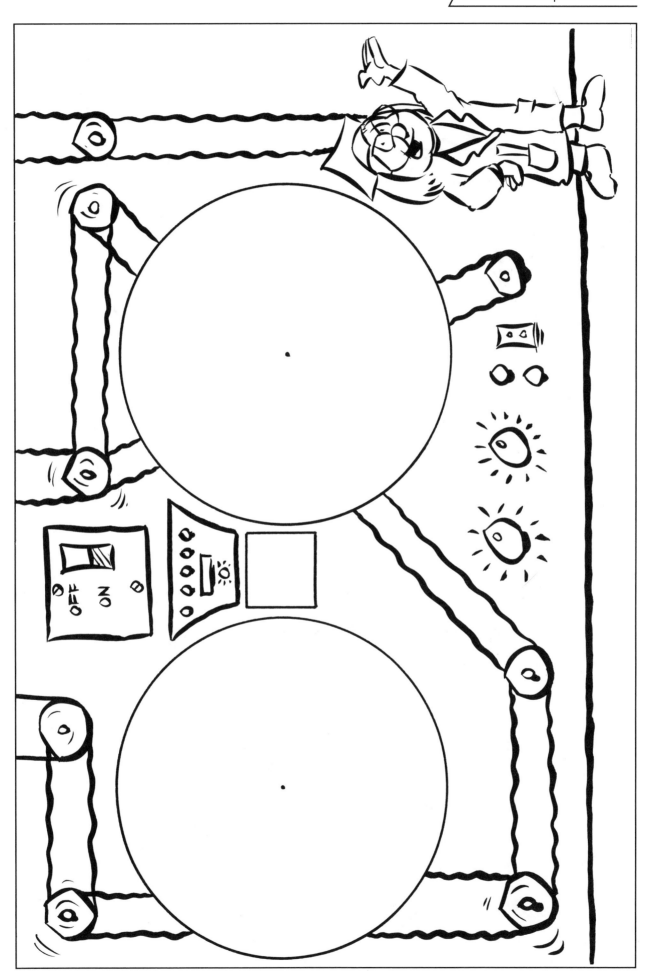

More long vowels

ew

Turn the wheel to find the words.

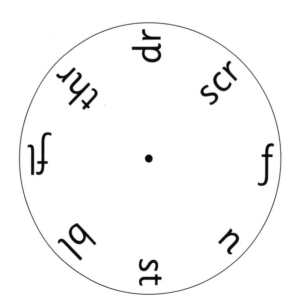

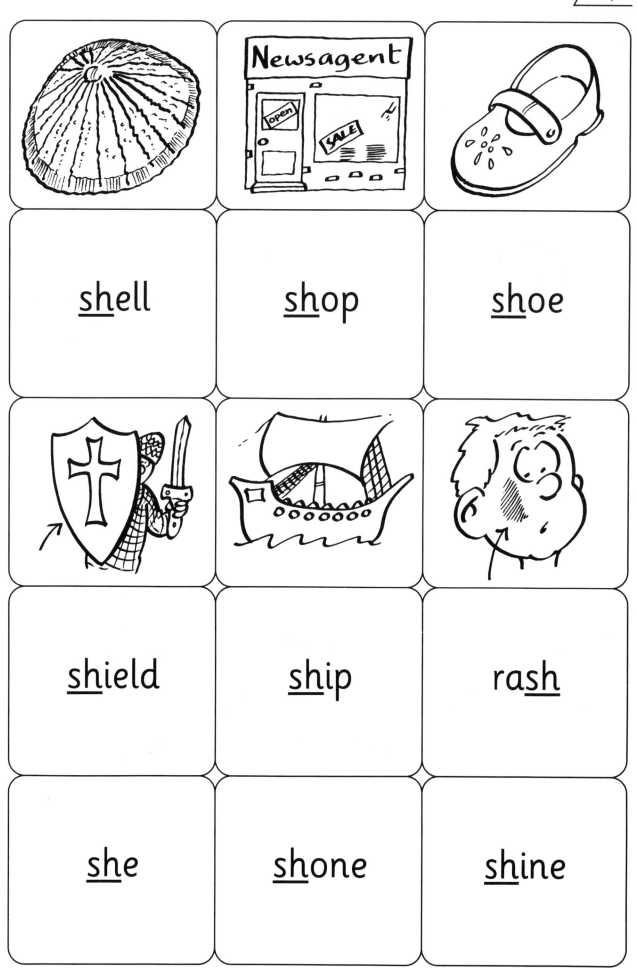

shell

shop

shoe

shield

ship

rash

she

shone

shine

Blends and digraphs

<u>th</u>imble	<u>th</u>orn	<u>th</u>irty
<u>th</u>umb	<u>th</u>irteen	<u>th</u>ree
<u>th</u>e	<u>th</u>en	<u>th</u>is

Blends and digraphs   **Copymaster 114**

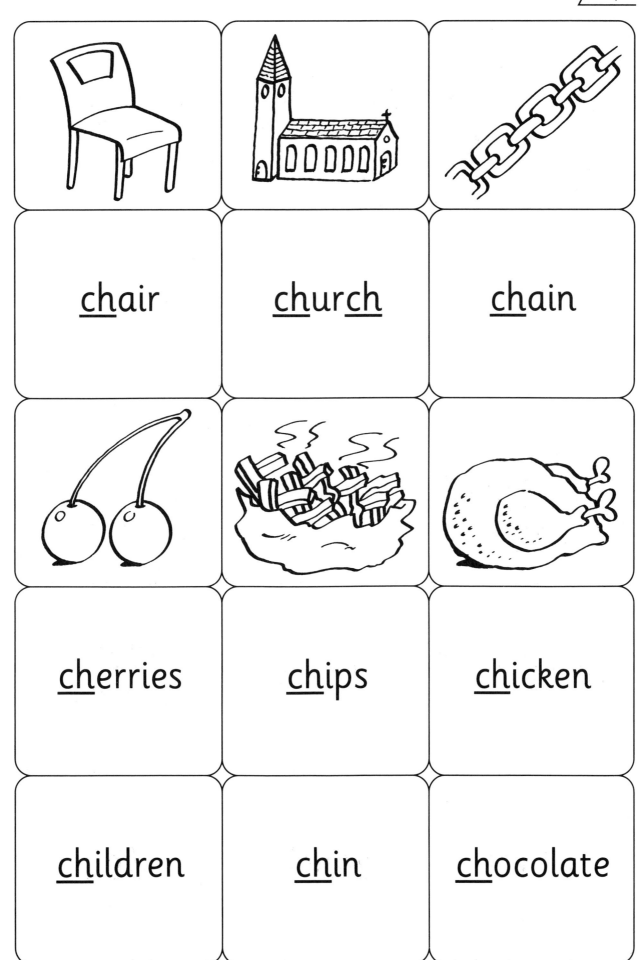

chair

church

chain

cherries

chips

chicken

children

chin

chocolate

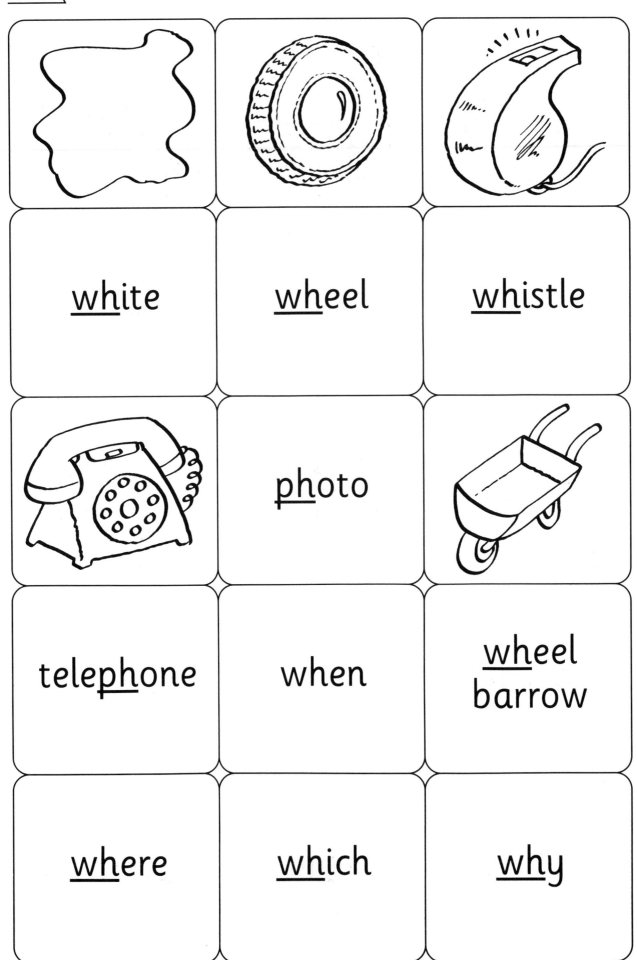

| <u>wh</u>ite | <u>wh</u>eel | <u>wh</u>istle |

| tele<u>ph</u>one | when | <u>wh</u>eel barrow |

<u>ph</u>oto

| <u>wh</u>ere | <u>wh</u>ich | <u>wh</u>y |

ch	ch	ch	ch	ch	ch	ch
th	th	th	th	th	th	th
sh	sh	sh	sh	sh	sh	sh
wh	wh	wh	wh	wh	wh	wh

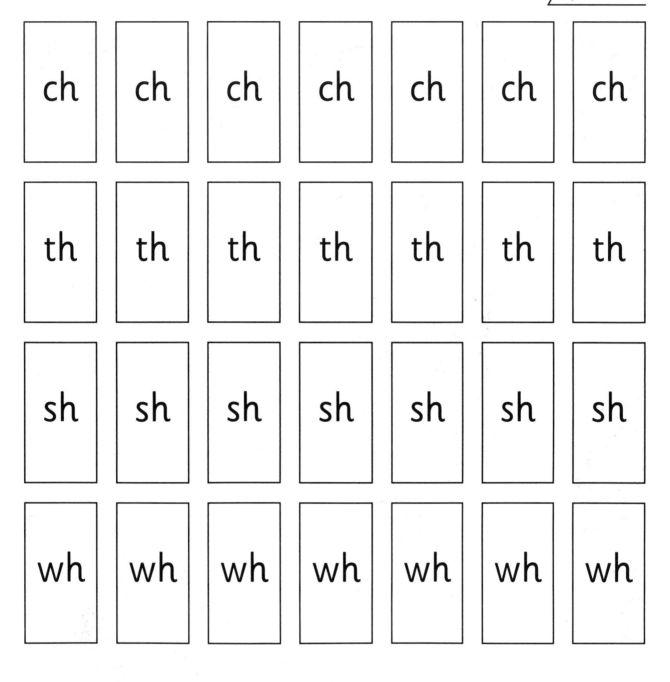

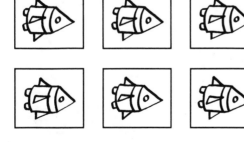

Blends and digraphs

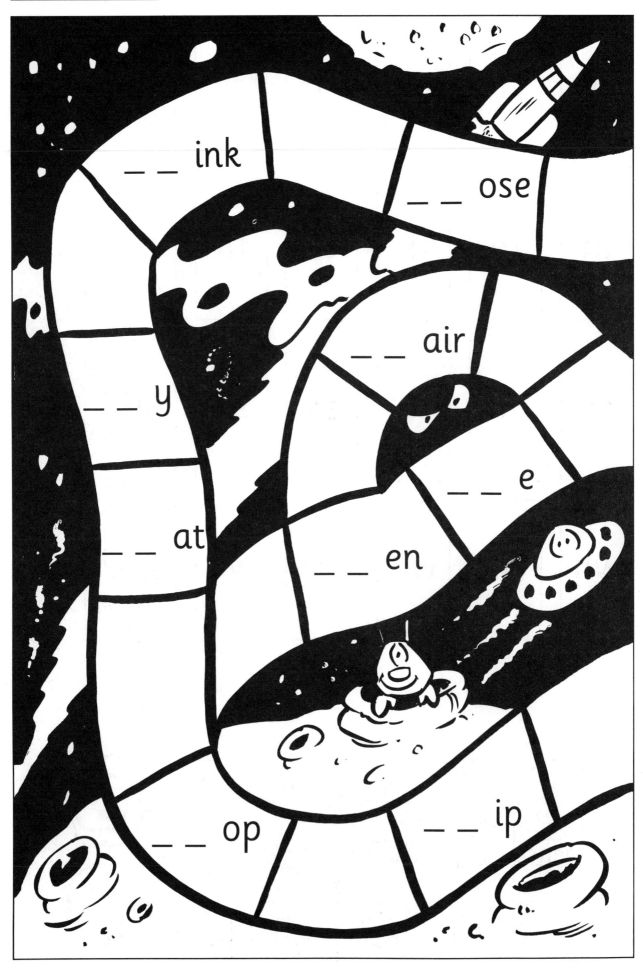

Blends and digraphs

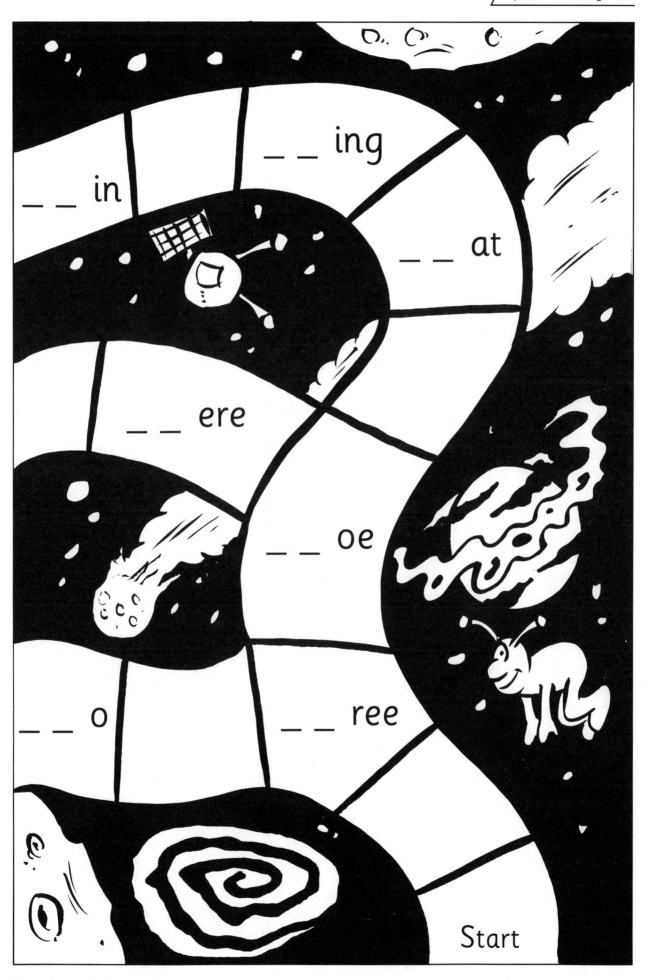

Blends and digraphs

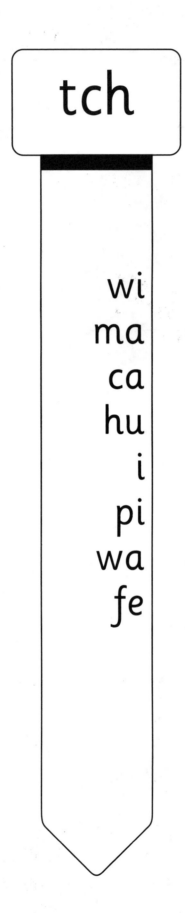

tch

wi
ma
ca
hu
i
pi
wa
fe

Help Wanda to find the words.

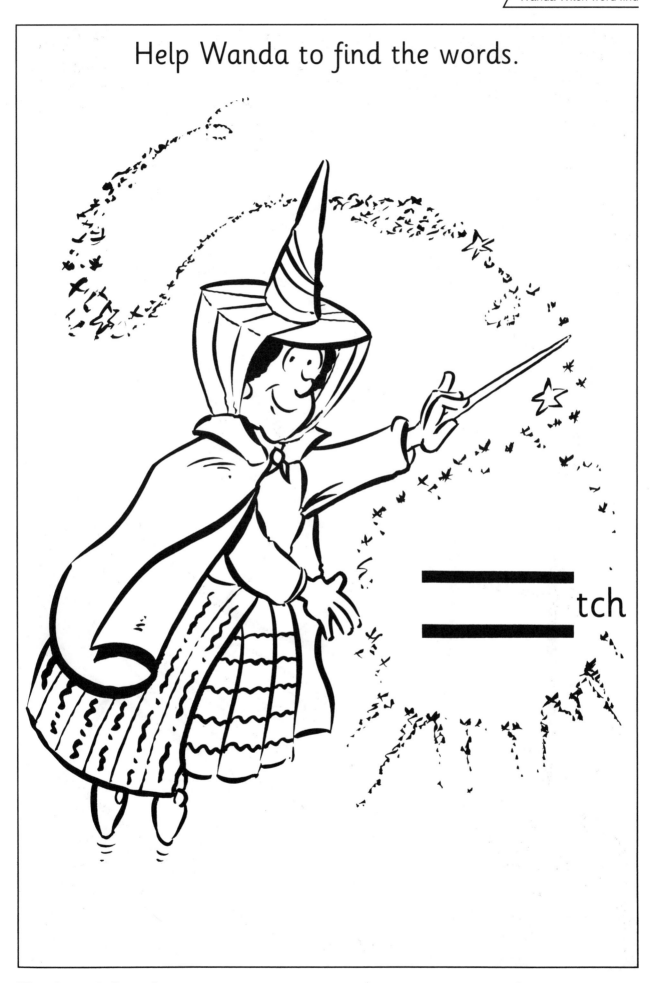

tch

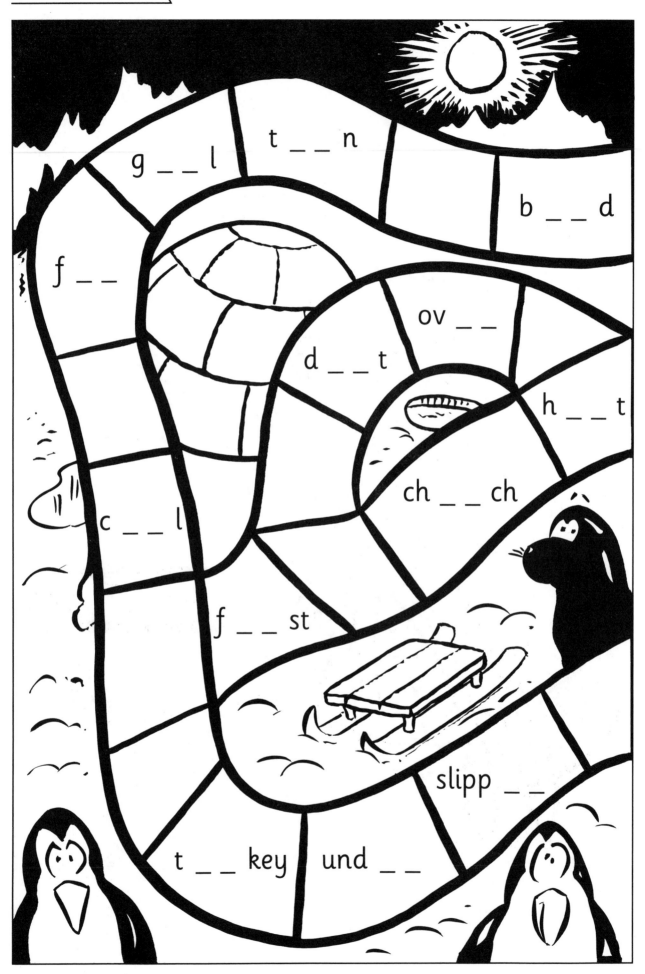

Blends and digraphs

f _ _

sh _ _ t

st _ _

wint _ _

dinn _ _

h _ _ dle

lett _ _

b _ _ n

bett _ _   th _ _ d

h _ _ d

Start

Blends and digraphs

Copymaster 123

er	er	er	er	er	er	er
ir	ir	ir	ir	ir	ir	ir
ur	ur	ur	ur	ur	ur	ur

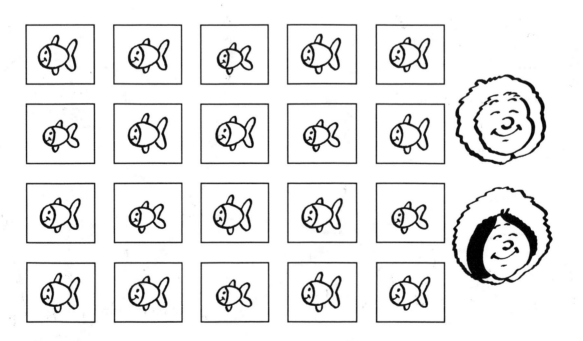

Blends and digraphs

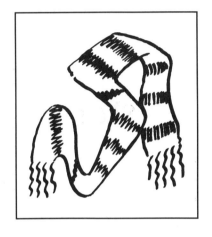

Blends and digraphs

Copymaster 125

	car	jar
scarf	farm	star
fork	torch	sport
horse	storm	cork

ff	ff	ff	ff	ff	ff	ff	ff
ll	ll	ll	ll	ll	ll	ll	ll
ss	ss	ss	ss	ss	ss	ss	ss

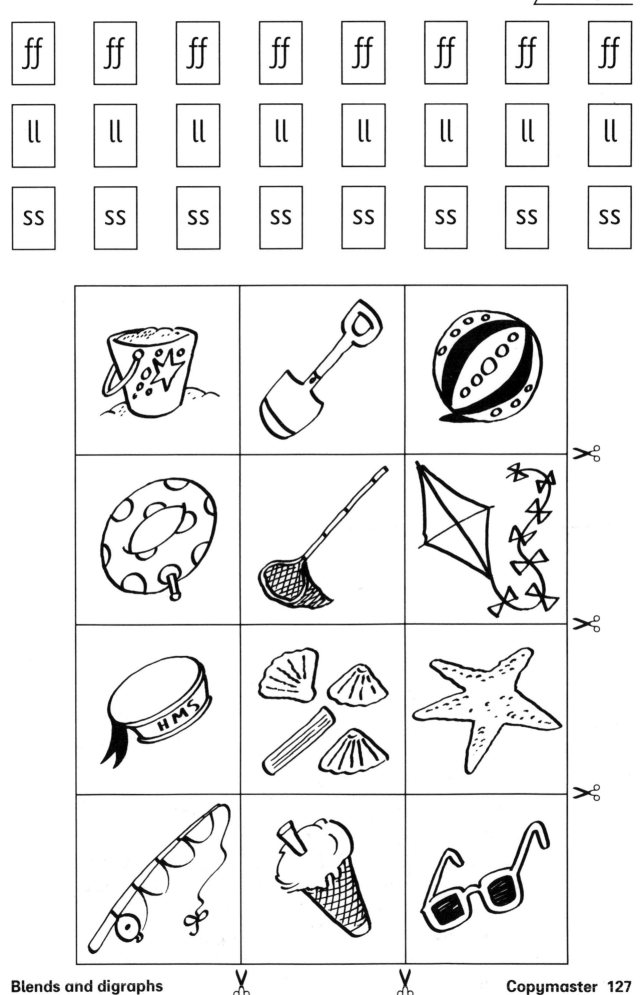

Blends and digraphs

Blends and digraphs

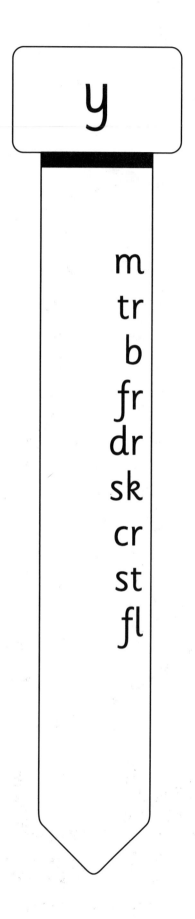

More long vowels

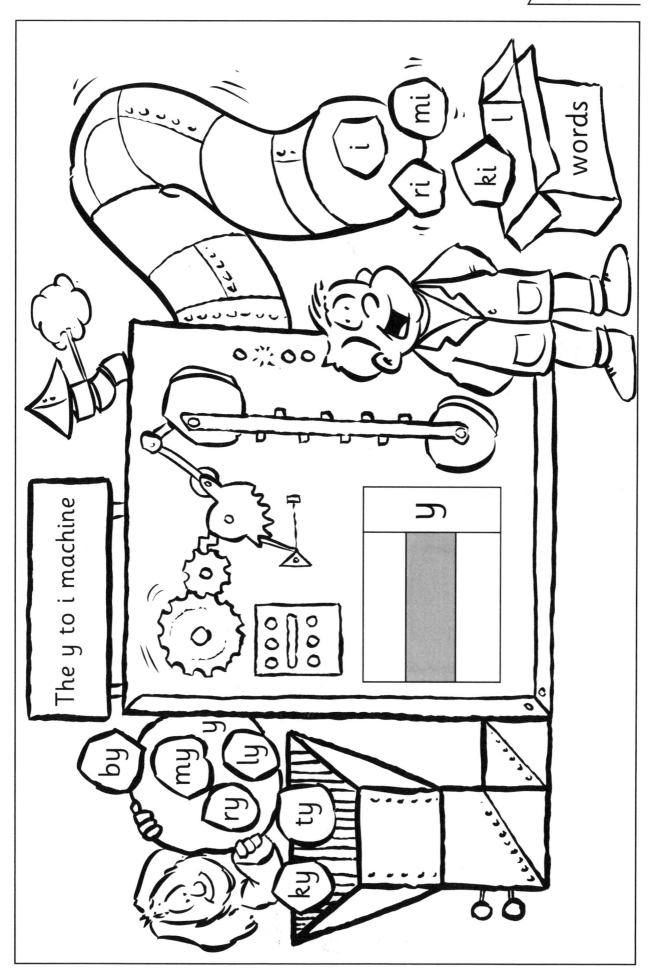

More long vowels

ay

Turn the wheel to find the words.

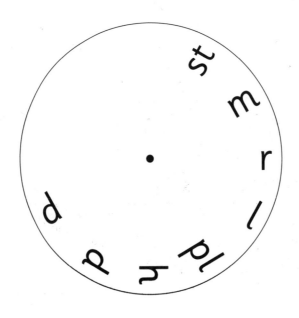

More long vowels

Short vowel sound at word ending – use ck.
Long vowel sound at word ending – use ke.

8 cake

sake 7

10 duke

shake 2

fake 5

take 3

4 Luke

6 make

bake 1

rake 9

Long vowel takes -ke

Short vowel and c sound at the end of a word takes – ck.

Short vowel takes -ck

Boys and girls come out to play

_ arol

_ en

_ at

_ ot

_ od

_ ettle

_ itten

_ ord

_ ar

More long vowels following c or k

Vowels following c or k

c	c	c	c	k	k	k	k
c	c	c	c	k	k	k	k
c	c	c	c	k	k	k	k
c	c	c	c	k	k	k	k
c	c	c	c	k	k	k	k

c is followed by a, o and u.

k is followed by the short e and i.

c is followed by a, o and u.

k is followed by the short e and i.

Vowels following c or k

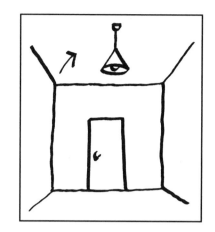

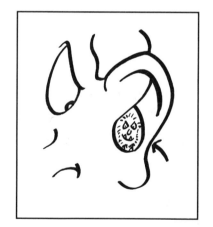

Softening of c and g

fence	parcel	ceiling
necklace	space	trace
ginger-bread man	badge	germ
large	gem	genie

Softening of c and g

ANSWERS TO WORD GAMES

Word list for Copymasters 36–37 short vowel sounds

pat pet pit pot put cat cot cut hat hit hot hut pan pen pin pun bad bed
bid bud dad did dud tap tip top dig dog dug lag leg log red rid rod

Word list for Copymasters 38–39 short vowel sounds

pat pet pit pot put cat cot cut pan pen pin pun hat hit hot hut lag leg
log bad bed bid bud red rid rod lad led lid dad did dud tap tip top

Word list for Copymasters 40–41 short vowel sounds

lad led lid lag leg log red rid rod dig dog dug tan ten tin ton dad did
dud bad bed bid bud pan pen pin pun hat hit hot hut cat cot cut pat
pet pit pot put tap tip top

Word list for Copymaster 44 words beginning with sl

slam slap slide slim slip sleep slipper slug

Word list for Copymaster 45 words beginning with gl

glad glass globe gloss glow glove glide glue

Word list for Copymaster 46 words beginning with pl

plan planet plant plate play please plod plot

Word list for Copymaster 51 words beginning with bl cl fl

bl	cl	fl
black	clip	flag
blue	class	flap
blot	clog	flash
bless	clock	flat
blink	cloth	flock
bled	cling	flip
block	cliff	fling
blank	clap	flesh
blur	club	flung
	clung	flush
	clown	flower

149

Word list for Copymaster 52 words beginning with dr fr tr

dr	fr	tr
draw	frog	tree
dress	frill	try
drip	fruit	true
drum	free	trust
drain	fridge	tried
drop	friend	train
drink	frost	tricycle
drill	fresh	tractor
dream	frown	trick
dragon	front	
	fried	

Word list for Copymaster 53 words beginning with br cr sl

br	cr	sl
bridge	crab	slow
bread	crash	slide
branch	cracker	slipper
brick	crust	slug
bride	crane	slot
brown	crook	slip
brush	crack	slam
brother	crown	slope
broken	crate	slit
bring		sleep
brain		

Word list for Copymaster 54 words beginning with sm sn sp

sm	sn	sp
smoke	snow	spade
small	snack	spear
smell	sniff	spank
smock	snore	speak
smug	snip	spell
smack	snail	spider
smile	snake	spin
smart	snap	spot
smash		

Word list for Copymaster 63 words ending in at et ot

at	et	ot
bat	bet	cot
cat	net	dot
fat	get	got
sat	met	hot
flat	set	lot
mat	let	not
rat	wet	pot
hat	pet	rot
pat	vet	

Word list for Copymaster 64 words ending in all ill an

all	ill	an
call	will	ran
ball	till	ban
all	ill	can
fall	bill	fan
stall	fill	man
tall	hill	nan
hall	kill	pan
wall	mill	ran
small	pill	tan
	still	van

Word list for Copymaster 65 words ending in and st ent

and	st	ent
land	fast	went
sand	mast	sent
band	last	lent
hand	past	bent
island	best	rent
stand	rest	tent
strand	nest	silent
	west	dent
	jest	
	list	
	fist	

151

Word list for Copymaster 66 words ending ng old nk

ng	old	nk
rang	fold	bank
hang	sold	monk
sang	old	sank
bang	told	tank
king	bold	link
sing	cold	pink
sting	gold	sink
ring	hold	wink
stung	scold	ink
		sunk

Word list for Copymaster 91 ow as in snow

mow row sow bow snow stow blow low

Word list for copymasters 100–101 ai ea or ee

ai	ea	ee
sail	seal	see
hail	leaf	bee
fail	bead	green
train	sea	heel
rain	heal	feel
grain	beach	beech
snail	sweat	sweet
	meat	meet
	feat	feet
		tree

Word lists for Copymaster 103

ee	ee	ea	ea
green	fee	meat	peak
sleep	feet	feat	peach
sleet	keen	sea	peat
see	keep	seat	teak
seen	sweep	leak	teach
seep	sweet	leaf	teat
thee	free	heat	tea
		pea	weak

152

Word lists for Copymaster 106

oo as in moon	oo as in moon	ou as in out	ou as in out
moo	balloon	sound	shout
mood	pool	found	loud
moon	root	hound	louse
moot	fool	house	lout
soot	foot	mouse	round
soon	food	mound	rout
spool	noon	cloud	ground
spoon		clout	grouse
			grout

Word lists for Copymaster 108

ar	ar	ow	ow
start	dark	cow	crow
stark	dart	cowboy	crown
jar	hark	cower	down
bar	hard	brow	dowel
bark	car	brown	dower
star	cart	how	flower
scar	card	howl	clown
scarf	smart	tow	flow
		town	flown
		towel	
		tower	

Word lists for Copymaster 110

ai	ai	oa	oa
frail	wail	road	loaf
snail	wait	roach	load
pain	said (not	float	goat
paid	correct sound)	coat	goad
pail	sailor	coach	goal
rain	sail	coal	broach
raid	main	boat	
rail	maid		
train	mail		
trail	chain		
trait			

Word list for Copymaster 112

blew drew few flew new screw stew threw

153

Answer list for Copymasters 118–119

ch	wh	sh	th	th
chip	who	ship	thin	think
chair	whose	shoe	that	then
chat	when	shin	thing	three
chin	why	she	there	the
chose	what	shy	those	thy
chop	where	shop	that	

Word list for Copymasters 120–121

witch match catch hutch itch pitch watch fetch

Word list for Copymasters 122–123 er ir ur all say er

er	ir	ur
herd	bird	fur
letter	fir	turkey
dinner	stir	church
winter	first	turn
over	dirt	burn
slipper	girl	curl
under	shirt	hurt
better	third	hurdle

Answer list for Copymasters 128–129 ll, ff and ss

ll	ll	ff	ss
bell	wall	sniff	brass
doll	full	muff	moss
fill	roll	toffee	miss
fall	mill	cliff	class
pull	mull	off	less
ball	well	cuff	mess
bull	still	stiff	dress
toll	call	puff	toss
		buff	fuss

Word list for Copymasters 130–131

my try by fry dry sky cry sty fly

Word list for Copymaster 132 ay words

day hay lay may pay play ray stay

Answer list for Copymasters 136–137 c or k

c	c	k	k
cat	cot	kilt	kennel
cord	cap	king	kid
curl	cop	kettle	Ken
cut	car	kitten	Katie
cod	Carol	kit	